THE 365 DAYS

THE
365
DAYS

Keith Gordon Irwin

ILLUSTRATED BY

GUY FLEMING

George G. Harrap & Co. Ltd

LONDON TORONTO WELLINGTON SYDNEY

First published in Great Britain 1965
by George G. Harrap & Co. Ltd
182 High Holborn, London W.C.1

Copyright © *1963 by Keith Gordon Irwin*

Printed in the United States of America

The illustrations on page 167 are from
Götter, Gräber und Gelehrte by C. W. Ceram.

CONTENTS

[v]

[vi]

PREFACE

A YEAR is the time swept out as the earth, a planet of the sun, completes its annual orbit about the sun. There are 365 days in that year, each day due to a spin of the earth on its axis. Around the year and the day man was to build his calendar. This book features the calendar story.

The calendar! Does not this seem a small topic around which to build a book—one whose contents would be exhausted in a very few pages? Such an attitude would be understandable if one looked upon the calendar as a mere arrangement of numbers and spaces set in the usual way as days, weeks, and months. But the calendar is more than a chart upon the wall. It is the gateway to all of the yesterdays, the moving stream of todays, and the tomorrows.

Calendar, the word, is from the language of the Romans. It came from the Greek word *kalend* which had the significance of "I *cry!*" It was the term used by the town crier of the ancient fortress city of Rome as he made his announcement about the days ahead. It was his duty to announce the beginning time of the months, to tell when the market days would be, and to state the day near the middle of the month when rents would be due. He took his orders from the Pontifices. These announcements were necessary because the Romans began each month with the appearance of the new moon as a thin crescent in the western sky just after the setting of the sun. From the day of one new moon to the next one was the moon-time of their calendar. (We write the "moon time" as *moonth—month*.) Two of these months are very nearly 59 days. The Romans used 30 days for the first month and 29 days for the second to reach the sum of 59 days for the two. But 59 was not perfectly correct. In sixteen times 59 days, or 32 months, one day had to be left out to keep the calendar in line with the actual movement of the moon. That still was not enough to keep the calendar in perfect agreement. An additional day had to be omitted occasionally. The varying lengths of the months, so produced, affected the time of the important day set at the middle of the month, called the Ides of the month. For each month the crier had to announce when the Ides would come.

We do not, today, follow the moon calendar of the early Romans. Our plan follows that of the year. Though we still use the word *month* it does not agree with the month of the moon. Our months are not of a single length any more than theirs were. In our calendar one day is added every fourth year but this extra day is left out at scattered points across the centuries, as it was in the year 1900, for example. Fortunately, we do not need a town crier to announce the beginning day for each month, the number of days it will have, or where the week breaks will be. For all its seeming irregularity, this calendar of ours is so closely adjusted to the year that we can follow its pattern with complete confidence.

For the life of today the newspapers and the radio take the place of the town crier. They will say nothing about the number of days in June or September. They will announce instead when school will open in the fall, when the banks will be closed, when the circus will come to town, and hundreds of other things that are associated with the days of the calendar.

There is far more to the full story of the calendar. The great calendar plan of Thoth, developed in ancient Egypt five thousand years ago, was used about three thousand years later by Julius Caesar in building a calendar for the Roman Empire. A great calendar plan for the seven-day week was conceived forty-five centuries ago—and such weeks are a part of our calendar of today.

Our calendar has its deficiencies. We are aware of that. Some people argue that we need to return more closely to the great calendar plans of antiquity. They offer for our consideration a World Calendar.

The story behind all calendars and ours in particular sweeps across five thousand years of history—a story that essentially is still incomplete.

I

A Background for the Calendar Story

ALL CALENDAR FORMS OF THE ANCIENT WORLD *were built around the simple time cycles of nature. Expressed in the ideas of today, the ancient calendar builders started with the day-night cycle of the earth spinning on its axis. To this they might add the cycle of the year resulting from the revolving of the earth about the sun. Or the day might be added to the cycle of moonlight produced by the revolv-*

ing of the moon about the earth. There was also another possibility. The day might be added to the seasons as marked off by differences in the length of day and night.

All of these basic calendar ideas were used in primitive time-recording arrangements. These arrangements were not necessarily crude. The American Indians kept an accurate record of passing days by cutting notches for each day on a stick or post. (The oldest Indian record preserved in continuous form apparently goes back for its beginning to A.D. 901.) The Hopi Indians of Arizona know the length of the year with high exactness; they count the year's beginning from that day in midwinter when the sun has reached its southernmost position and starts climbing northward along the horizon. The Navaho sheepherder with his flocks on the lonely hills counts time precisely in terms of the lunar month of 29½ days. Only the cycle of the seasons had not been built into a trustworthy calendar by the farmers of a more primitive world. The reasons are obvious. The dates for planting and harvesting vary somewhat with the years, even for the same location. There is a wide variation for widely separated locations.

Carefully devised calendars became a necessity with the growth of complex civilizations. By that time it had been discovered that the day, lunar month, and year were completely independent in their time schedules. *No calendar could include all of these time units of nature in a single simple plan. Even a plan that contained but two of the three time units would run into grave difficulties.*

Leaving the calendars themselves for later, we shall be focusing attention in the pages that follow upon nature's time cycles and their relations to each other.

The Zodiac : Sagittarius

I

TIME CYCLES

AND THE

HEAVENLY BODIES

FROM THE BEGINNING of human history man believed two things to be true about the sun, the earth, and himself. First, he thought that the sun traveled around the earth. Second, he thought that the particular land where he and his clan lived was the center of creation, since any view from the hills of that land showed the horizon spread out equally all around. (You and I might believe such things, too, if wise men of recent centuries had not demonstrated that both ideas are incorrect.)

The Earth as a Planet of the Sun

IN THE PRESENT CHAPTER we put down the relation of the earth to the sun and moon as developed by modern astronomy. These facts explain the time cycles of the day, seasons, year, and lunar month.

You learned in school that the earth is a planet of the sun. Light and heat from the sun reach half of the earth at any one time, the other half being then in darkness. Since the earth turns on its axis, the half now illuminated is trailed by the part now in darkness. In that way day and night follow each other endlessly. But the revolving earth also makes a complete swing through space around the sun and back every year to the same position in relation to the sun. That swing around the sun does not in itself account for the seasons. The earth's axis is not perpendicular to the path of the earth's swing; it is tilted to one side. In the summer the northern end of the tilted axis is angled toward the sun. In another half year the effect is reversed. But always the part of the earth that is tilted toward the sun will have long days and short nights, while the other part will have long nights and short days. At two times in each year the days and nights will be exactly equal in length. The astronomer uses the word *equinox* ("equal night") to indicate each of these locations in the progress of the year. In the northern hemisphere, that of March 21 is called the *spring equinox*, the one of September 23 the *autumn equinox*. In winter when the nights have reached their greatest length, the daytime

THE AXIS OF THE EARTH'S ROTATION IS INCLINED $23\frac{1}{2}°$
TO THE PLANE OF ITS ORBIT AROUND THE SUN.

*The earth at
winter solstice*

*The earth at
summer solstice*

$23\frac{1}{2}°$

Arctic circle: zone of continuous night

Winter solstice (December 22)
LONGEST NIGHT, SHORTEST DAY

Autumnal equinox (September 23)
EQUAL DAY AND NIGHT

Spring equinox (March 21)
EQUAL DAY AND NIGHT

Summer solstice (June 21)
LONGEST DAY, SHORTEST NIGHT

Arctic circle: zone of continuous daylight

THE VARIATION IN THE LENGTH OF DAY AND NIGHT
RESULTS FROM THE INCLINATION OF EARTH'S AXIS.

sun is at its lowest position in the sky. For a single day the sun seems to stand still in relation to the day's length, then sunrise will come a bit earlier than before. This time—December 22—is known to the astronomer as the *winter solstice*, the word solstice meaning "sun standing still." A matching time comes in summer when the night is shortest and the daytime sun is highest in the sky. This is the *summer solstice* of June 21.

Timing Effects of the Earth's Elliptical Orbit

IN ITS MOTION ABOUT THE SUN the earth does not follow a simple circular path but travels along an ellipse. In middle January the earth is three million miles closer to the sun than in late July. Because of the elliptical shape of the orbit there is an inequality in the lengths of the four seasons as those seasons are divided by the equinoxes and solstices.

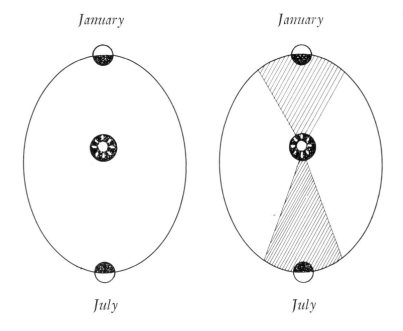

January   *January*

July   *July*

You can see why from these diagrams. The first shows the sun in relation to the earth's elliptical orbit. (The orbit's elongation is exaggerated.) The top of the figure indicates the position of the earth in middle January, the bottom in late July. It is a mathematical feature of the ellipse that a body moving along an elliptical path sweeps out an area within the figure that remains constant for equal times. In the next figure a period of sixty days is shown for a time of the year near January and also for the year near July. The areas swept out within the figure appear in shading. These *areas* will be *equal*. The upper shaded area has less depth; its advance along the orbit is correspondingly greater. This means that a larger portion of the total orbit *length* will be covered in January than in July in a period of sixty days. The third figure places the seasons of the year in position over the elliptical orbit. To the right and left are the times of the equinoxes, above

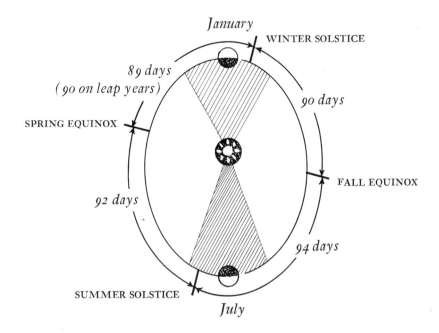

and below are the solstices. The figure shows how un-even—in terms of days—the four seasons arc.

You can determine for yourself the lengths of the seasons from the dates of the equinoxes—September 23 and March 21—and of the solstices—December 22 and June 21. Autumn, from September 23 to December 22, is 90 days. Winter, from December 22 to March 21, is 89 days, or 90 days in a leap year. Spring, from March 21 to June 21, is 92 days. Summer, from June 21 to September 23, is 94 days. This variation in the number of days for the seasons as marked off by equinoxes and solstices was to be a source of difficulty in calendar building as we shall see at a later point.

The Moon as a Satellite of the Earth

THE ORBIT OF THE MOON, as a satellite of the earth, is slightly elliptical. And it is angled about five degrees from the earth's orbit about the sun. As a result, the moon does not follow a well-beaten path across the vault of the heavens. At times the full moon rises to the south of due east and stays in the south part of the sky as it moves on through the night. At another time it will rise to the north of due east and stay in the north part of the sky as it moves onward. And, be-tween the other positions, it can rise in the exact east and set in the exact west.

Had the earth and moon been without this angled difference in their paths of motion there would be an eclipse of the sun every month, as the moon got into

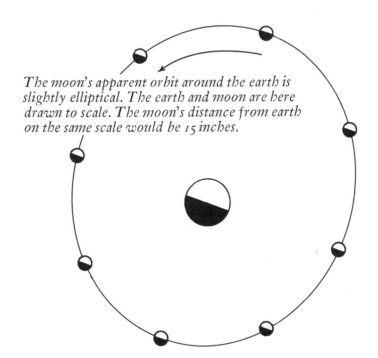

The moon's apparent orbit around the earth is slightly elliptical. The earth and moon are here drawn to scale. The moon's distance from earth on the same scale would be 15 inches.

The moon's orbit is inclined 5° to the plane of the earth's orbit around the sun.

the space between us and the sun. There would be an eclipse of the moon each month, as the moon passed into the shadow thrown by the earth. But with the angle at which the moon's orbit is set, eclipses are not frequent.

Time Cycles of Moonlight and Tides

As A SOURCE OF LIGHT the moon is not like the sun. The sun is a radiant source of light; the moon merely reflects some of the sun's illumination that shines upon it. As the moon swings around the earth

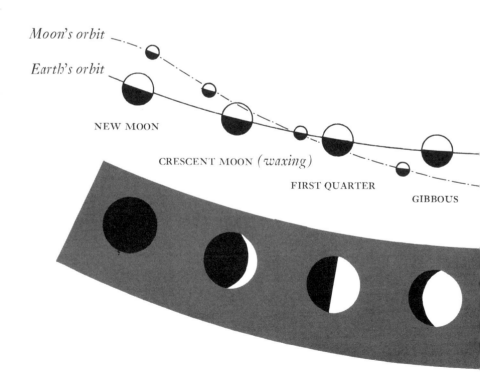

Moon's orbit

Earth's orbit

NEW MOON

CRESCENT MOON *(waxing)*

FIRST QUARTER

GIBBOUS

only the half of the moon that is toward the sun is lit up by the sunshine. If the dark side of the moon is toward us as it moves across the sky, we do not know that the moon is there. A few days later we can see a thin sliver of light in a crescent form, appearing near the western horizon for a brief time after the sun has set. This is the crescent moon. About fourteen days later the illuminated part faces toward us, the great ball of the full moon rising in the east as the sun goes down in the west. After the night of the full moon, the moon rises later in the evening and gradually the part lit by the sunshine is less seen from the earth. Finally, as a

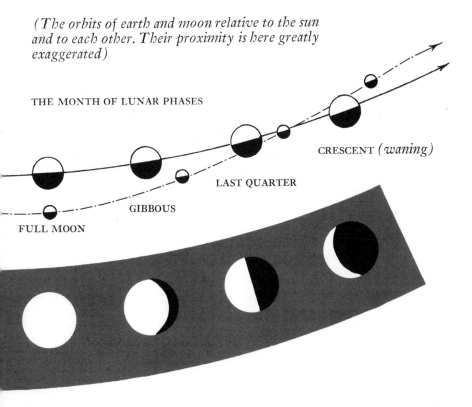

(The orbits of earth and moon relative to the sun and to each other. Their proximity is here greatly exaggerated)

THE MONTH OF LUNAR PHASES

CRESCENT *(waning)*

LAST QUARTER

GIBBOUS

FULL MOON

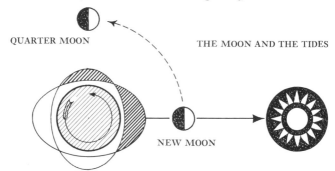

NEAP TIDES *(least range) occur when the attraction of moon and sun act at right angles.*

QUARTER MOON

THE MOON AND THE TIDES

NEW MOON

SPRING TIDES *(greatest range) occur when the attraction of moon and sun act in the same plane.*

thin sliver of the illuminated moon, its bulging part toward the east, we can see the sickle of the dying moon in the early dawn before the sun rises.

This cycle of moonlight keeps repeating over and over as the year passes. But the moon's motion as a satellite is *independent* of the earth's rotation on its axis. So the moonlight cycle, or lunar month, as the astronomer calls it, does not come out as a whole number of days, nor even as an exact fraction over and beyond a whole number of days. Written with five figures the value of the lunar month is 29.531 days.

Since the rate of the earth's rotation on its axis is *independent* of its motion through space as a planet of the sun, and both are *independent* of the moon's motion as an earth satellite, we have a total of three values that contain fractions of an incommensurate size.

Solar year = 365.2422 days
Lunar month = 29.53059 days
Lunar months in solar year = 12.36827

Use will be made of these number values in the discussion of the difficulties of calendar building.

The moon plays a dominant part in another cycle. As the moving satellite passes high over the earth the water of the ocean rises, pulled by the moon's gravitation. After the moon has passed, the water settles down again. Then the water rises again when the moon is just halfway around the earth from where it was before. The earth rotates on its axis as the moon revolves about the earth. The moon therefore "circles" the earth every 24 hours 50 minutes, the water of the ocean being caused to rise and fall in a steady rhythm. To this rhythm the lives of the creatures of sea and shore are sensitively set.

The Zodiac : Capricornus

2

THE

TIME CYCLE

OF LIFE

LIVING THINGS ARE ENDOWED with a strange and marvelous ability to handle their life activities with a clock-like precision. Potatoes sprout in the bin in February. That is the time for which their built-in chemical alarm is set; December will not do. Lilacs have an appointed time for blooming; no coddling of the plants in a heated greenhouse will change the time. The wild asters by the roadside bloom when the lengthening nights of autumn approach; they seem to wait for these days. Such examples can be extended almost endlessly.

Running through them is the general conclusion: each organism has its own built-in timing system.

Some Features of the Human Timing System

THE HUMAN TIMING ARRANGEMENT may best be approached from the observation point of a newborn baby. With his first cry, life for him as an individual suddenly begins. We can compare the little body to a wonderful watch—a watch guaranteed to run a lifetime, an instrument warranted to grow bigger and stronger as the days pass. Man-made watches need to be wound to start them and keep them in action. How different the little human body! Once started it needs no rewinding. It is complete with its own built-in oscillator that is sensitive immediately to every need for faster action, completely automatic in its control. This marvelous timing and control system is a part of creation.

Of all the people of the ancient world, a wise physician of long-ago Egypt seems to have been the first to understand the major features of the life-timing plan of the human mother in relation to her baby and herself. Known to the Egyptians as Thoth, he was to be worshiped as a minor god a thousand years after his death.

Thoth found that all babies, whether born in the long days of summer or the short days of winter, whether born under a crescent moon or a full moon, had pulse rates close to those of other babies. In comparison with older children, he found that babies had a faster pulse, they moved more quickly, and breathed more rapidly. He also found that a woman's pulse rate was about a sixth faster than a man's. He seems to have suggested that the normal pulse rate for a woman was 100,000 beats for a day-night period of time, that value being very nearly 70 beats per minute by our way of measuring time.

Life-Cycle Periods and the Year

WE TURN NOW FOR A MOMENT to the life activities of domestic animals. The time of mating and the time of carrying the young before birth fit in an exact way into the span of the year. Lambs and calves are born in the spring. The time of birth does not creep closer to the year's beginning, or draw farther from it. The relation with the year is perfect. Among wild animals, the grizzly bear's cubs are born in pairs but only in alternate years; it follows a life-and-fertility plan spread with exactness across two years.

The Importance of an Ancient Paternity Case

APPARENTLY THE EARLY EGYPTIAN CALENDAR devised by Thoth about five thousand years ago was built around the feminine time period of a twelfth of the year. We find a story to that effect. The Roman historian Plutarch recounts a tale of ancient records told to him by the chief priests of an old Egyptian temple.

The story relates that Thoth was called as an expert

in a certain important paternity case. Ra, an early king of Egypt, was extremely jealous of his attractive wife Nut. When her child was born he refused to see either his wife or the baby, declaring that the child was not his. She had been unfaithful—so he claimed. She denied it. Thoth, who seems to have known her well, defended her.

It was brought out in the trial that the husband, in calculating when the child's birth would have been had he been the father, had used a time of nine moonlight cycles, allowing thirty days for each cycle. Thoth produced evidence that the feminine fertility cycle follows a slightly longer period, one that fits exactly into the year. It was further brought out that the year was five days longer than Ra had supposed it to be. The child was born, according to Thoth, at the normal time. The defense won.

An outcome of the case was that Thoth became very much interested in the possibility of designing a calendar that would state correctly the relations between the life-cycle periods of animals and people, and the year's length.

You may be wondering whether the tale as presented here is truth or fiction. It is both. The details of the handling are mine, for Plutarch is brief. I believe that my interpretation is trustworthy. Here is a translation from the Latin of Plutarch as given by Sir James George Frazer.[1]

[1] Frazer, Sir James George, *The Golden Bough* (a series of volumes on ancient religions, etc.), The Macmillan Company, New York, 1936, third edition, vol. II, page 6.

Ra's year of 12 moon cycles having 30 days each

|←   360 DAYS   →|

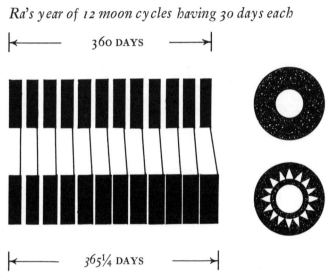

|←   365¼ DAYS   →|

Thoth's year of 12 equal fertility cycles equals the true period of the earth's revolution around the sun.

When the sun-god *Ra* perceived that his wife *Nut* had been unfaithful to him, he declared with a curse that she should be delivered of the child in no month and no year! But the goddess had another lover, the god Thoth . . . and he playing at draughts with the moon won from her a seventy-second part of every day, and having compounded five whole days out of these parts he added them to the Egyptian year of three hundred and sixty days.

11

Features of the Ancient Calendars

AHEAD OF US IS THE STORY *of how different groups of people in the ancient world fashioned calendars to meet their special needs. Many arrangements were tried.*

Yet we must recognize the astronomer's verdict: No calendar can blend into a single, simple composite the natural time units derived from the independent motions of a spinning earth, an earth whirling through space around the sun, and the moon as a satellite of the earth.

The Zodiac: Aquarius

3

A CALENDAR

FOR EGYPT

Tʜᴇ ɴɪʟᴇ ᴠᴀʟʟᴇʏ ɪs ᴀ sᴛʀᴀɴɢᴇ, ɪɴʜᴏsᴘɪᴛᴀʙʟᴇ ʟᴀɴᴅ.
A small group of people worked their way into that
valley over five thousand years ago, though it is almost
a mystery how they were able to survive. Then, later
—almost suddenly—such people found out how to turn
the unfriendly land into a place of pleasant, disaster-
free living. A few centuries later came, almost as suddenly, a period of great cultural and industrial advance.
The production of the Egyptian calendar was a feature of that advance.

The Strange Valley of the Nile

THE NILE RISES IN THE LOFTY MOUNTAINS of central Africa, where in winter an enormous accumulation of snow covers the high plateaus. Water derived from the snow fields runs northward toward the distant Mediterranean Sea, following a little rift in the surface of the continent. This portion is the Nile River. Majestically, almost without ripples, the mighty body of water goes on its way. Along its course the Blue Nile adds its water, the combined streams passing across a vast expanse of unbroken desert. Near the southern border of Egypt the flowing water enters a narrow valley with rocky cliffs on either side. The view is that of a desert landscape, with no vegetation of any kind along the cliffs. The flat bottom of the narrow valley is, at most, but a few miles wide. Before the coming of man to the valley land the only green color was that of scattered clumps of river reeds and papyrus plants rooted in the mud of shallow parts of the river.

As the river nears the Mediterranean it passes beyond the last of the cliffs. In the Delta, where the river deposits its mud to clog the main channel, the stream breaks up into small, sluggish waterways half-choked with reeds. Scattered among the reeds in ancient times were patches of pasture grass, some gnarled and stunted trees. Flocks of birds nestled in the river reeds or moved on long legs in the river mud.

In the lofty plateaus of central Africa the summer

THE VALLEY OF THE LOWER NILE

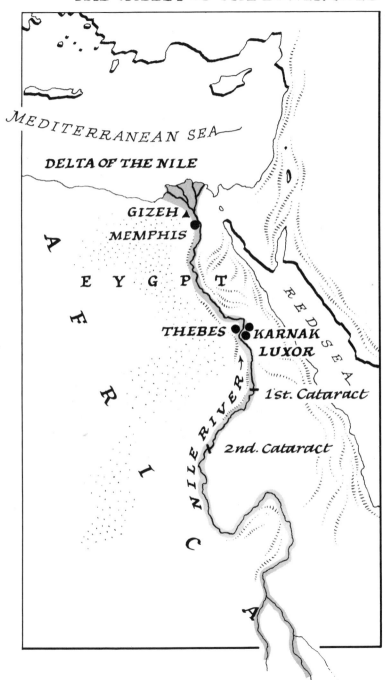

MEDITERRANEAN SEA

DELTA OF THE NILE

GIZEH
MEMPHIS

A
F
E   Y   G   P   T
R
I
C
A

THEBES KARNAK
LUXOR

RED SEA

NILE RIVER

1st. Cataract

2nd. Cataract

heat melts the deep snows, sending down the river a surge of water that overflows the river banks. And because the rift in the continent's surface, along which the river flows, slopes so gently toward the distant Mediterranean, the overflowing water from the melted snows turns the Nile into an elongated lake. The shoreland, now submerged, turns to mud. And mud it continues to be for about two months, until the floodwaters pass and the great river returns to its banks. As the water subsides the fields that have been muddy soon dry out in the desertlike air. If it were not for man's efforts, the valley would return to desert again.

Our attention now turns to the small family group that, at an early date, must have worked into the valley from the Delta country. Apparently they possessed a small herd of goats, a container full of wheat kernels, and garlic, leeks, and onions in bunches. There was no true pasture upon which the goats could feed, but the lively animals doubtless secured a scanty living from the river plants that grew in clumps in the mud of shallower parts of the river. For their own food supply the women seem to have planted the garlic, leeks, and onions in trenches beside the river, watering them by hand. The wheat was scattered in shallow furrows, covered over with soil, then watered by hand. Additional items of food were the birds' eggs taken from nests in the reeds and fish caught in the shallow waters.

In this food growing as we have conceived it, little or no use had been made of the floodwaters that overflowed the lands beside the river. Then came a great discovery. If the goats were driven back and forth

across the muddy lands just as the floodwaters sub-
sided their hoof marks roughened the surface. The
resulting little mounds and depressions stayed damp
much longer than did the undisturbed mud, which
soon caked in the sun. Kernels of wheat tossed on the
thoroughly damp roughened ground could be trodden
in by driving the goats back and forth. The seed would
germinate, grow rapidly, and ripen. There was no need
for watering by hand. The raising of wheat was thus
made easy. Any family, working as a group at harvest
time, could have an abundance of grain for food. And
the goats got the straw, chaff, and dropped grain as
their share of the harvest.

Once well established, the lives of the men and
women of early Egypt went on pleasantly and
serenely. The valley had no earthquakes or violent
storms. There was no famine danger, for the river never
ran dry. True, the high-water mark of the floodwaters
might fail to reach the normal level, leaving some of
the higher wheat fields dry for that season. For such a
mild emergency, a reserve of seed and food was kept
on hand.

A Big Man with Big Ideas

About the year 3400 b.c. a new historical
era began for Egypt. Hieroglyphic writing was invented. Activities not known to an earlier Egypt were
pictured by artists on the walls of temples and tombs.
These things, in a general way, have been credited to
the guiding efforts of Menes, first of the dynastic
rulers of ancient Egypt.

A Calendar for Egypt

A Tomb for Khufu

TWO OR THREE CENTURIES LATER Khufu (or Cheops as Greek historians spelled his name) came to the Egyptian throne. Menes and his immediate successors had undertaken great public works. Khufu's public-works project was a giant tomb for himself.

This tomb is known today as the Great Pyramid. Built of great blocks of limestone, it is as high as a forty-story building and each side of its square base is as long as two football fields. It is not a crude, poorly designed, or weakly constructed monument. Its form mathematically precise, it was wonderfully built, on a rock base. Not a single crack formed as the centuries passed.

The king had very evidently been greatly excited over the work in astronomy then under way among the temple priests of Egypt. He had a telescope built into the pyramid as it was under construction. This telescope did not have lenses and other parts to be found in the great telescopes of today; it had only the tubelike channel aimed at the sky. The outside opening was on the triangular side of the structure that faced the north. The lower end, where the observer would be, was in the burial chamber deep in the huge rock tomb.

To one looking outward, the telescope channel was aimed at that special region of the sky which always seems to be at rest as the field of the stars turns in slow rotation. Judging from the slope of the channel, the king was watching the pole star of that time of history. Doubtless he thought of it as peering at him through the telescope, and he was certain that it would be waiting for him with its tiny but steady light when he awoke again in his life-after-death.

A Calendar for Egypt

Measurement Systems in Ancient Egypt

THE GREAT PYRAMID DEMONSTRATES the ancients' accomplishments in technology and astronomy.

People who could design and construct such an enormous structure and carry out the needed measurements with such striking skill were great engineers. That they used a system of measurement units that can seem completely modern to us was discovered by the great English Egyptologist Flinders Petrie toward the close of the past century. The basic small unit of length was the *zebo*, about a third of an inch in size. Larger units were equal to 10, 100, 1,000, and 10,000 zebos—a *decimal* plan. The decimal plan was extended to container sizes for the measuring of grains and liquids. Thus liquids were measured by a main unit of 1,000 cubic zebos. The units of weight also had a decimal relation to each other.

To these people all measuring was simply an extension of counting. Counting was done by tens, hundreds, thousands, and, possibly, ten thousands; measurement values were handled in the same simple way.[1] It need not be surprising, then, that the measurement of time, when it was developed, used decimally related units.

[1] Details of the ancient Egyptian measurement system are given in Irwin, Keith Gordon, *The Romance of Weights and Measures,* The Viking Press, Inc., New York, 1960, Chapter 2.

Use of Astronomy in Getting the Year's Length

KHUFU'S TELESCOPE WAS NOT USED to get the year's length—an important value in calendar building. That value had been found by a use of simple astronomy perhaps two centuries before the time of Khufu.

The priests of some temple such as that of Osiris knew that Sirius, brightest of all the fixed stars, appeared in summer, rising above the horizon just before sunrise. Carefully watching day after day, they awaited its appearance. On that day its flash could be seen just for a moment, then the flash would fade as the sun rose. On the next day the flash would remain longer, for the star was getting ahead of the sun. Just a few days after this, the Nile floodwaters started to spill over the river banks and the people had to hurry to get their goats and possessions to higher ground.

This relation of Sirius to the rising floodwaters was used by the temple priests as a sure way to predict the time of the Nile overflow. When the star appeared flood warnings were sent out. (Actually, there was a slight variation in the time of overflow, but the plan worked well.) After a half century or so of such watching, it became evident that the time of rising of the star could itself be predicted. The number of days between two such risings was 365, and a little more. In four years the little more amounted to a full day. This gave their value for the year's length as 365¼ days. The true value, as given on page 16, is 365.2422 days. Their value was less than an hour wrong in five years.

FLOOD

PLANTING

HARVEST

The Egyptian Calendar of Thoth

THE FACT THAT THOTH, the wise physician, developed a calendar plan for Egypt has already been mentioned.

His calendar arrangement is a solar calendar, built around the solar year of 365¼ days. The autumn equinox time, which we refer to as September 23, was the beginning point of his year. This choice was quite logical for Egypt, since that was the time of planting and the return of the river to its banks after the flood-waters had passed. The time of the spring equinox was a second time of importance in his plan for the year. The number of days from the autumn equinox to the spring equinox, as determined by counting them, was 180. The number from the spring equinox to the autumn equinox was greater; it was 185¼. The distribution of the 180 and the 185 days was handled by using the life-cycle period of 30 days, which Thoth considered extremely important. (See page 22.) For this thirty-day period he used the Egyptian word that corresponded to our word *month* (or "moonth"), but this month had no specific relation to the lunar month of the moonlight cycle, which was disregarded.

The half of the year for the time after the autumn equinox was put down, then, as 180 days and divided into six 30-day months. The other half, of a little over 185 days, was counted as six 30-day months followed by 5 extra days. In his plan the months were numbered but not named; the extra days were named but not numbered.

The extra days were placed at the end of the year; that is, by our way of putting down the dates, from September 18 through September 22. The names for these were those of deities worshiped at the Temple of Osiris: (1) Osiris, (2) Horus, (3) Set, (4) the goddess Isis, (5) Nephthys. It is uncertain whether Thoth had a special place in the calendar for the extra day added every fourth year or whether it was counted as a double day for Nephthys.

It might be assumed that Thoth's plan of bunching

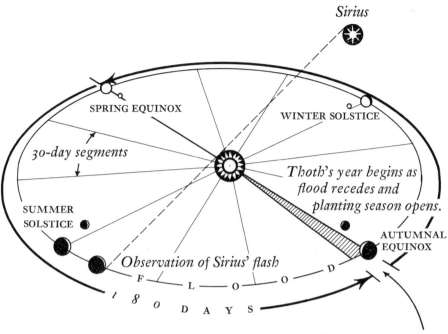

Sirius

SPRING EQUINOX   WINTER SOLSTICE

30-day segments

Thoth's year begins as flood recedes and planting season opens.

SUMMER SOLSTICE

Observation of Sirius' flash

AUTUMNAL EQUINOX

F — L — O — O — D

1 8 0 D A Y S

5 extra days were added to the second cycle of 180 days, 6 on every fourth year.

Thoth Calendar Arrangement

AUTUMN EQUINOX			SPRING EQUINOX		
Month 1	30 days		*Month* 7	30 days	
2	30	"	8	30	"
3	30	"	9	30	"
4	30	"	10	30	"
5	30	"	11	30	"
6	30	"	12	30	"

Extra days   5; 6 every fourth year

THOTH'S SMALL TIME UNITS

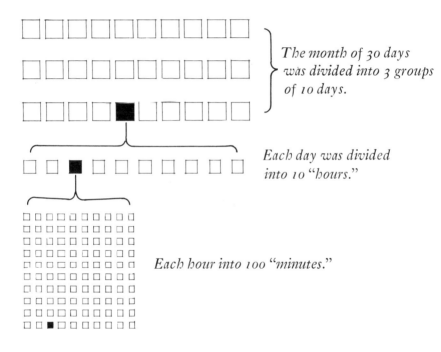

The month of 30 days was divided into 3 groups of 10 days.

Each day was divided into 10 "hours."

Each hour into 100 "minutes."

the five extra days at the end of the year was illogical in that those days were not considered a part of the feminine life-cycle period. (It was apparently in this time of extra days that Nut's baby was born—a matter of importance in the ancient paternity case.) Yet nature operates in essentially that way. Because of the elliptical orbit of the earth around the sun the summer period is dragged out by those five days, though the carrying of young before birth fits the year's plan with exactness.

A Decimal Plan for Small Time Units

THOTH, AS A SEPARATE UNDERTAKING, extended the calendar plan to take in small time units. He used decimal relations between the units, producing an extremely simple timing plan.

---

1. The month of 30 days was divided into three 10-day groups.
2. Each day was divided into 10 "hours," each "hour" into 100 "minutes," each "minute" into 100 "seconds."

By this plan there were 100,000 "seconds" in the time from one midnight to the next midnight. (By today's plan there are 86,400 seconds in that length of time. Our timing arrangement does not follow a simple decimal system.)

Revival of the Egyptian Calendar and Thoth's Time Measures in the Time of the French Revolution

You may wonder why Thoth's simple calendar and time-measurement plan have not been revived in present-day use. They were revived, once.

On April 7, 1795, the National Convention of Revolutionary France passed a law that put into effect a new French calendar and a new French time-unit plan. The calendar—the work of a committee composed of a teacher, an astronomer, two mathematicians, and a poet—was that of ancient Egypt with no changes made except in names.

Thus the year started with the autumn equinox; it had 360 numbered days divided into 12 months of 30 days each; in addition to the numbered days were 5 extra days that were named but not numbered—these were placed at the end of the year, just before the time of the autumn equinox.

The names for the extra days substituted French words for *ideas* in place of the names of the five Egyptian deities that Thoth had used: (1) the virtues, (2) the genius, (3) the labor, (4) the opinion, (5) the rewards.

The decimal plan for small time units was also taken directly from that of Thoth as used in ancient Egypt, again with a mere change of wording into French.

The month of 30 days was divided into three 10-day groups.

The day was divided into 10 new hours, each new hour into 100 new minutes, each new minute into 100 new seconds—giving a total of 100,000 new seconds per day.

The new—but, also very old—plans for the calendar and small-unit timing remained in use but twelve years. The law was repealed on December 31, 1805. The difficulty? *The law had abolished the seven-day week,* replacing it with the ten-day division of the month. Religious observances, market days, and old festivals had been built around the seven-day week. For twelve years everything had been in confusion!

The Zodiac: Pisces

4

THE MOONLIGHT
CALENDAR

The Land of the Fertile Crescent

To the northeast of Egypt, northward and eastward from the coastline of the Mediterranean, is a sweeping curve of land that fringes an interior desert. Historians call this area the Cradle of Civilization. Ruins of ancient cities have been uncovered there, some of them already a thousand years old when Menes became king of Egypt.

As shown in the map, the area takes in a long curving sweep of plowable land, called the Fertile Crescent, that starts in the hill country of Palestine at the southwest, passes to the northeast across Syria, goes on to the hill country of western Iran, ending near the Persian Gulf. The space within the great curve of crop land is today an almost pathless desert. At an oasis in the western part is the city of Damascus, the oldest occupied city in the world. East of Damascus is the immense, almost flat, rainless valley of the Tigris and Euphrates rivers. Fed by the melting of mountain snows and by rains in the high hills at the north and northeast, the two rivers—one at each side of the valley—move sluggishly southward through the desert-dry air. The rivers join before the Persian Gulf is reached.

For the arable lands of the Fertile Crescent there was generally adequate rain for crops. For the northern part of the Crescent the rains were apparently greater than they are today, but in all parts the usual farms were small, their pasture areas scattered across the hills.

Upon these scanty acres of farm lands, and along the caravan routes that circled the Crescent, a civilization had developed that was old even in the days when Khufu was building the Great Pyramid. The basis of this early civilization was the development of wheat from a wild grain plant of the meadows. In that same general period, barley was produced from another wild grain plant. Grapes, olives, and figs were modified into quality fruits from hillside vines and trees. Cattle, sheep, and goats had already been domesticated and handled in grazing groups, forming another feature of the great advance.

Invention carried the new civilization forward. The

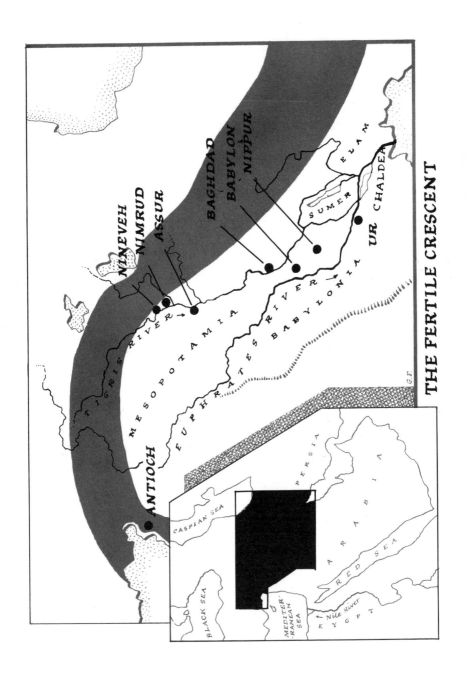

THE FERTILE CRESCENT

NINEVEH
NIMRUD
ASSUR

BAGHDAD
BABYLON
NIPPUR

ELAM

SUMER

UR CHALDEA

TIGRIS RIVER

MESOPOTAMIA

EUPHRATES RIVER

BABYLONIA

ANTIOCH

G.F.

CASPIAN SEA

PERSIA

ARABIA

RED SEA

BLACK SEA

MEDITER-RANEAN SEA

Nile River

EYGPT

wool from the sheep when clipped and combed was twisted into thread, and the thread woven into warm woolen clothing. Flax, which had been a wild reed-like plant of the ravines, had fibers in its stalks. These fibers were found to be tough but resilient and could be used for linen threads in making linen clothing.

These advances made up the early agricultural revolution. The food, clothing, and shelter needs for the families of the Fertile Crescent were being met for the first time in an ample way, year after year.

In this general period in or near the Fertile Crescent, the primitive moon calendar of the shepherd and villager was transformed into the calendar of moonlight.

The Primitive Moon Calendar

EARLY MAN HAD USED the moon's motion and the changes in its illumination as the "Clock of the Night Sky." The lonely shepherd watching over his flock through the night, the tent dwellers moving their animals to new pastures in the cool of the evening, the guards protecting a village against intruders—all these knew the time story of moonlight. They knew just where to look for the crescent-shaped new moon. They were aware that the full moon would appear about eleven days after their first sight of the new crescent moon. They knew also about how many days it would be before the sickle of the dying moon would be awaiting the coming of the sun in the eastern sky. They would have known also that the exact appearance and position of the new moon would not be repeated at the time of the next new moon, and that the number of new moons in a year might be twelve or it might be thirteen. But no successful attempt had apparently been reached in the early days of human history to build a calendar around the cycle of moonlight that would be accurate in its predictions.

Adjustments of the Moon Calendar for a Tribal Group

FOR THE ACTIVITIES OF A WHOLE TRIBE, the primitive moon calendar was not adequate. It could not predict, months in advance, the exact date of the first appearance of the crescent moon or the exact night when the full moon would be at its brightest. The difficulty lay in the incommensurate relation of the lunar month to the days within it.

As noted in an earlier chapter, the time from one new moon to the next is 29.53059 days, or, for convenience, 29.53 days. It was the fractional part of the leftover day that made calendar building difficult. Observations, repeated thousands of times by tribal priests, had shown that the position in the western sky and the thinness of the crescent new moon corresponded more closely to the one of *two* months before than to the one in between. There was, however, no exact duplication. We can explain the situation in this way. The length of two months is 59.06 days. If the figure came to an even 59 days the crescent moons of alternate months would match each other perfectly in the sky

DIFFICULTIES INVOLVED IN KEEPING THE DAYS

ALIGNED WITH THE CYCLE OF MOONLIGHT

ACTUAL PERIOD: *59.06 days*

ASSIGNED PERIOD:

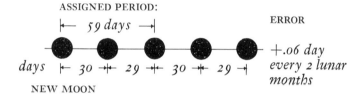

ERROR

+.06 day
every 2 lunar
months

days ⊢― 30 ―⫶⊦⫶― 29 ―⫶⊦⫶― 30 ―⫶⊦⫶― 29 ―⊣

NEW MOON

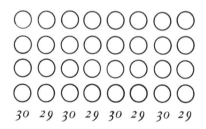

30 29 30 29 30 29 30 29

*In 32 lunar months this error
equals .96 day. One day is
added to the 32nd month,
making it 30 days in
length rather than 29.*

*The error of −.04 day every
32 lunar months accumulates to
−1. day in 800 lunar months
and must be subtracted
from the last month.*

position and crescent thinness. The additional fraction of o.o6 of a day spoils the perfect matching. The second one of the two crescents has a *slightly* thicker appearance. In 32 lunar months the gain amounts to almost exactly a whole day. Really the gain is 0.96 of a day. So in 800 such months the difference between 0.96 of a day and a full day introduces another whole day's error.

The calendar of moonlight, as it was developed, needed three types of adjustments in order to fit days and months together. To handle the approximate time of two months as 59 days, the first month in a series would be put down as 30 days, the second as 29 days, the third as 30 days, the fourth as 29 days, to be repeated endlessly. To handle the gain of one day in 32 months the 32nd month was given 30 days, not 29 as would otherwise have been the case. Finally, to take care of the day lost every 800 months that month was given 29 days, not 30 as would have been the case except for this correction. That was the time plan of the calendar of moonlight. Its manipulation was placed in the hands of the tribal priests.

The Handling of the Year

COMPLICATED AS THE CALENDAR WAS in connection with the lunar month and the days within it there was even greater complication in the handling of lunar months and the year.

As recorded in a previous chapter, there are 12.368 lunar months in the year. This makes the year about

11 days longer than 12 lunar months. Two years then would be about 22 days longer than 24 lunar months, and three years about 33 days longer than 36 lunar months. But 33 days is longer than a lunar month. Actually three years turns out to be close to 3½ days longer than 37 lunar months. Were we to count the lunar year as 12 lunar months then a simple relation becomes evident: 33 lunar years are almost exactly equal to 32 ordinary years. So in a century of time keeping there would be just three times when the two kinds of years would start out together.

The religious calendar of the Mohammedans adheres to a year of 12 lunar months. As stated before, this year is about 11 days shorter than the solar year, which governs the time of planting and harvest. Let us suppose that the first day of their lunar year fell this year on January 1. Next year it would be back in December. In three years it would be near the end of November. In 33 lunar years the starting point of the year is back at January 1 again.

The ancient Greeks used the calendar of moonlight but handled the lunar year in a different way. Wishing to keep the first month of that year from wandering far from its initial position, they gave two possible lengths to the year. Sometimes it had a length of 12 lunar months, sometimes a length of 13 lunar months. In any series of years, the first and second years would be given 12 lunar months, the third year given 13 such months. This did not bring their year plan into any exact relation to the solar year. By using seventeen 12-month years and ten 13-month years in a series of 27

THE REGRESSION OF THE LUNAR NEW YEAR

IN RELATION TO THE SOLAR YEAR

The lunar year being approximately 11 days short of the true period of earth's revolution, the lunar new year regresses at that rate, reaching its original position relative to earth after 33 years.

The solar year equals 12.368 lunar months.

DIFFERENCE EQUALS APPROXIMATELY 11 DAYS.

The year of 12 moonlight cycles

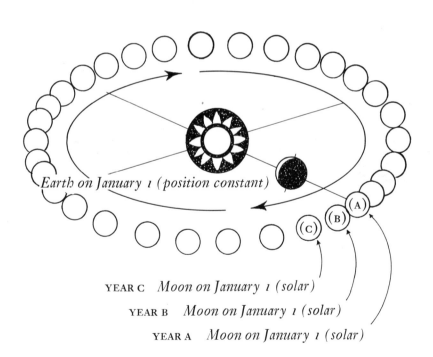

Earth on January 1 (position constant)

YEAR C *Moon on January 1 (solar)*

YEAR B *Moon on January 1 (solar)*

YEAR A *Moon on January 1 (solar)*

years the two methods of measuring time reached final agreement. But for the years between, the Greek plan was only in approximate agreement with the solar year. A further point needs to be added. With so many adjustments needed to handle the mixture of 29- and 30-day lunar months and 12- and 13-month lunar years, skillful supervision was very important. Errors resulted in calendar confusion. Further supervision was needed to divide the month for market-day purposes. A division into half months readily handled the 30-day month, each half receiving 15 days. For the 29-day months the two half months in the month were uneven, being 15 and 14 days. Should the division be extended to quarter months two lengths would be needed. For the two-month period taking in a 30-day month followed by a 29-day month, the quarter-month handling would be as follows: 8 days, 7 days, 8 days, 7 days, 8 days, 7 days, 7 days, 7 days. The town crier carried out the necessary control. At each month's beginning he announced when the market days would be held.

The Zodiac: Aries

5

THE CALENDAR

OF THE

SEVEN-DAY WEEK

THE THIRD OF THE GREAT CALENDAR PLANS developed near the eastern end of the Mediterranean built a man-designed time unit into the time of the solar year of 365¼ days. That time unit was the seven-day week. The year was equal to 52 weeks with 1¼ days left over. The 52 weeks could be divided into four equal parts for the four seasons. Four of these weeks would make a "month" of 28 days and there would be 13 of these "months" in the year. *Mathematically* the division was fascinatingly simple, *practically* it was excellent.

It cannot be determined with any certainty where or when the use of seven in this way began, but the idea of seven as a "magic number" that could unlock the secrets of the year goes back at least three thousand years in the land of ancient Mesopotamia. In that early time a true calendar of the year had not developed around the seven-day week. The explanation is simple. The matter of the 1¼ extra days was ignored, the weeks moving on steadily. As a result the 52-week year was out of step with the solar year of 365¼ days. In eight solar years the year-of-the-weeks was 10 days behind; in a century the difference was virtually a third of a year.

Moses Does Some Planning

THE CREDIT FOR CHANGING the year plan of the week into a fine calendar arrangement can be given to Moses. The time was about 1500 B.C.

Moses—adopted by an Egyptian princess, raised in her household, and trained in a temple school—must certainly have acquired a knowledge of simple astronomy. It would have included Thoth's calendar, which had three outstanding features: it started the year at the time in autumn when the lengths of day and night are equal; it divided the year evenly into months; it handled the 5¼ days left over as a group that was not counted as a part of any month.

After Moses led the Israelites from Egypt, he devised a calendar plan carrying some of the features of the calendar of Thoth but built around weeks rather

than months. He wished the plan to be distinctive—
and it was. The seventh day of the week was to be
called the Sabbath and handled as a holy day. This religious emphasis was important. Following the plan
used by Thoth in Egypt, the year was to start in
autumn at the day when night and day are equal. At
the end of the 52 weeks the counting of days would
stop and the remaining day, or two days in a leap
year, would be used as a time of celebration. In this
simple way the year of the weeks was blended perfectly with the solar year. As to the year itself, it

MOSES' CALENDAR OF 52 WEEKS HAVING 7 DAYS EACH

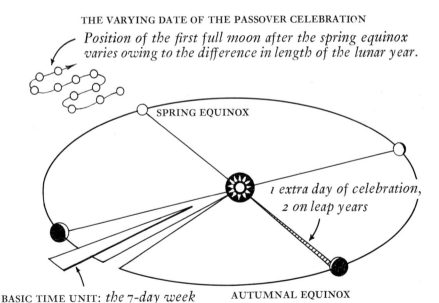

THE VARYING DATE OF THE PASSOVER CELEBRATION

*Position of the first full moon after the spring equinox
varies owing to the difference in length of the lunar year.*

SPRING EQUINOX

*1 extra day of celebration,
2 on leap years*

BASIC TIME UNIT: *the 7-day week*   AUTUMNAL EQUINOX

would always begin on the first day of a week and end on the last day of a week. Each of the four seasons had the same number of weeks; each season, then, would begin on the first day of a week and end on the last day of a week. (It would be possible to handle a period of 4 weeks or 28 days as a "month," with 13 months to the year, though Moses does not seem to have made use of this arrangement.)

A comment should be made about the seasons under Moses' plan. The year began with the autumn equinox, and closed the autumn season 91 days later. The winter season and the spring season were also 91 days each. The summer season, including the 1¼ extra days, was 92¼ days in length. The actual division of the year by the equinoxes and solstices comes very close to 90 days each for autumn, winter, and spring, and close to 95 days for summer. Thus Moses' arrangement was not significantly different from the natural one.

The Feast of the Passover

OVER AND OVER, Moses said:

REMEMBER THE SABBATH to keep it Holy.

He did not say, "Remember to ask the priests as to when the Sabbath will be." His simple plan of the seven-day week required no priestly interpretation or guidance.

But the priests of Israel did have their part to play

in connection with the great festival of spring known as the Passover. The people of Israel, under the leadership of Moses, had escaped from Egypt at the time of the full moon that came just after the spring equinox. The old festival of spring, common to many tribes, had been reorganized by the Israelites as the great national celebration of that exodus from Egypt. The re-enactment of the various events of that exodus called for the strong light of the full moon to illuminate the area being used. The date of the celebration was established as the first Sabbath after the first full moon after the spring equinox. The actual date varied in its position in the year, for the movement of the moon is independent of that of the earth around the sun. It was a duty of the priests to determine in advance when the Passover would be celebrated. The matter required a knowledge of the calendar of moonlight. So, to a small degree, the Israelites kept time by two calendars: the *civil calendar* of week days, and the calendar of moonlight, or *religious calendar*, as applied to special religious festivals.

The Zodiac: Taurus

6

TIME IDEAS FROM THE EUPHRATES VALLEY

THE BACKGROUND OF THE CALENDAR STORY now shifts to a new period of history for southwestern Asia. It is to be a time of large cities, of marching armies, of long trade routes, of merchants dealing in products never handled before.

The Euphrates River

To us, the cities of this new historical period can seem strangely placed. Babylon, Nineveh, and Ur were large cities built on treeless stretches along ancient rivers. Not far away were the wastes of trackless deserts. All three were in the valley of the Tigris and Euphrates rivers. Babylon and Ur were on the Euphrates, the great river that begins in the mountains of present-day Turkey. Leaving the mountain base, the river starts southward toward the distant Persian Gulf. As the valley surface is broad and nearly flat the water flows sluggishly. Since the valley is without rain the land across which the river moves is a continuous desert.

About five thousand years ago some people from the outside managed to secure a foothold in the lower part of the valley, in the section called Chaldea in the Bible record. They found fish in the marshes. Garlic and onion plants were placed in shallow ditches near the Euphrates and watered from the river by hand. Small fields of grain were planted close to the river in autumn, watered by hand, and harvested in the spring. Larger fields of grain could be handled by using cattle for plowing and also to raise water from the river to irrigate the crops. They found that the more water lifted, the larger the crop yield; the larger the yield, the more people could be fed and the more cattle could be handled.

There were, however, many difficulties to overcome. We can list several: the fearful, enervating heat of summer; the lack of grass as pasture for the cattle; the ever-present possibility of salt, driven by strong winds from the Persian Gulf, making the crop land worthless; the normal shortage of water in the river when it was needed for the autumn seed-planting time. Disaster might strike in the spring just as the grain would be ripening. The melting of snow in the mountains to the north or the run-off from heavy spring rains could send a sudden deluge of floodwaters down the Euphrates to destroy the fields of ripening grain, ruin the houses, and drown the cattle. Occasionally a whole city would be affected. Ur in Chaldea had to be abandoned after a great flood filled the river channel beside the city with mud and sand and gouged out a new channel about three miles away.

In a reverse sort of way, a great flood changed Babylon from a mere hamlet to the site of a great industrial city. As a hamlet it was located on a small branch of the Euphrates at the point where a well-traveled caravan route crossed the valley toward Nineveh. The flood changed the branch stream into the main river channel along which river boats could run. So Babylon became a center for the caravan trade to Nineveh as well as a center for river traffic. In time, certain special features contributed to the city's growth in an industrial way. One was the introduction of the date, the fruit of the date palm. This tree sets fruit only in a region of high temperatures, such as Arabia. Where the conditions are correct, the trees bear heavily, and the fruit does not spoil after being dried in the sun. Babylon, with its caravan and boat facilities, profited enormously from the date trade. Another feature in the city's growth came from the skill of the metal workers. They had perfected the making of superior bronze castings and the production of fine bronze tools and

instruments. A few centuries later the workmen of Babylon knew the secret of turning common iron into fine tool steel. Again, out from the city went the industrial products by caravan and river routes. And back to the city by those same routes moved the metals or metal ores that would go into more industrial products.

Against this background of advance, we will note the progress made in Chaldea and Babylon in time measurement.

Chaldea and the Calendar

TODAY, THE LONG-ABANDONED CITY of Ur in the desert of the lower Euphrates Valley, in what was once the land of Chaldea, is a flat-topped mound. Under the gray dust have been found the utensils of home, palace, and temple that were left behind when the city was abandoned after the great flood. Written on clay that had been baked into bricklike hardness were the records of nearly five thousand years ago.

From such records we know that men from long-ago Chaldea visited ancient Egypt. Perhaps they went to see Khufu's Great Pyramid. Perhaps these men stayed in Egypt long enough to learn the language of that country so they could converse with the temple priests. These matters are guesses. But the calendar plan they carried back to Chaldea was, unmistakably, that of Thoth.

There was the same number of days in the year: 365¼. This had been checked from the rise of a certain bright star just before sunrise. (In Egypt the star was Sirius, in Chaldea it was Aldebaran.) The first 360 days were numbered and divided into 12 months of 30 days each.

The remaining days were named but not numbered and were grouped at the end of the year just before the autumn equinox. (In Egypt the naming was, in order: Osiris, Horus, Set, the goddess Isis, Nephthys. In Chaldea the order was: Nergal, Nabu, Marduk, the goddess Ishtar, Ninib.)

(Incidentally, our way of measuring the size of a circle as 360° represented their way of indicating the size of the year in calculations. The ° was the simple picture of a sun and stood for "day." So 360° meant a year of 360 days.)

The Chaldean Plan for Small Time Units

THERE IS NO EVIDENCE that the decimally arranged plan of Thoth for the parts of a day reached Chaldea. There is abundant evidence, however, of the use of a comparable plan that seems to have been substituted for it.

The *Thoth arrangement*, previously given on page 39, will be repeated here to show the nature of the substitution:

Day divided into 10 "hours";
each hour divided into 100 "minutes";
each minute divided into 100 "seconds."

The *Chaldean arrangement*—familiar to us, for it is our plan as well as theirs:

Day divided into 24 hours;
each hour divided into 60 minutes;
each minute divided into 60 seconds.

A Pathway Among the Stars

THE NEXT PART OF THE CALENDAR STORY from the ancient lands along the Euphrates belongs to the astronomers.

By the year 800 B.C., the astronomers of busy industrial Babylon had completed their studies of the motions of the planets across the night sky. At least fifty of the brightest fixed stars had been studied, their motions followed, their star maps drawn. The men doing these things were not amateur "watchers of the sky" but trained and skillful observers. They were not, of course, aware that the stars are very far away and resemble our sun. They were not aware that the motions that the stars appear to have as the night passes on come from the daily revolution of the earth on its axis; not aware that the seeming movement of the entire vault of the starry sky with the seasons is the result of the inclination of the earth's axis; not aware that the apparent wandering of the sun among the stars as the year passes is connected with the motion of the earth in its annual revolution about the sun; not aware that the reason for the summer's dragged-out number of days is the elliptical nature of the earth's orbit.

In Babylon, the astronomers bending over their star maps, having no inkling that the apparent motion of the stars is due to earth motions, tried to explain the passage of the seasons in what to us may seem a fantastic manner. They *assumed* that the sun in the period of a year followed a long curving trail out among the stars, the curving trail being completed as the sun returned to its starting point. They considered that the sun along the trail was visiting among the star groups that we call constellations. It would stay near one constellation for thirty days, then move along to another constellation for thirty days, finally getting back to the starting point after visiting, in order, twelve different constellations and spending thirty days with each— except for the constellation reached near the end of summer. There the sun put in five extra days. It was in this way that they explained Thoth's calendar months, which they also used.

The twelve "visited" constellations were named. The one having the bright star, Aldebaran, in it was named the *Bull*. They fancied that they could make out a bull's picture in the star arrangement, bright Aldebaran being the bull's eye and other stars marking the tips of the two horns or the shape of the head and shoulders. Another constellation, consisting of a total of eighteen stars, was called the *Fishes* because the astronomers fancied that the eighteen stars formed a picture of two separate but intertwined fish in the sky.

The twelve "visited" constellations were all named after something that had life, with one exception. Seven represented animals. The Twins, the Virgin, the Archer, and the Water Bearer completed the list of living things. The Balance was the additional object. Aristotle, the Greek scholar, called them the *zoidion* or "little animals." The twelve are now said to form the band or belt of the zodiac.

One point should be added. The various constellations of the zodiac band did not occupy spaces of identical size in the night sky. The astronomers widened or narrowed the "influence" of each to a twelfth of the year. They did more. With an accuracy of measurement unknown before, they worked out the effect of the elliptical orbit of the earth, as we would

The Bull

express it, upon the twelve portions of the year that formed the months. Their results may be summarized briefly as follows: For the half of the year from the autumn equinox to the spring equinox the months had a length of 30 days each except that the fifth month (which corresponds to our February) was better given as 29¼ days. The other part of the year had a total of 186 days or 6 more than 30 days for each month. They were spread out over the summer months, though the greatest concentration appeared in what would be our August and September. Thoth had put these extra days at the year's end, as a group.

AT THIS POINT we close the ancient calendar plans developed in southwest Asia and Egypt. It may be well to list them for further reference.

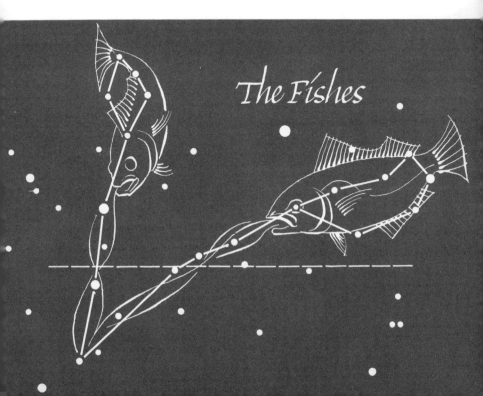

The Fishes

1. The Egyptian calendar plan of Thoth, developed about 3000 B.C. The beginning of the year was set at the time of the autumn equinox. The year was divided into 12 months of 30 days each, a group of 5 days, or 6 on leap years, being added but not counted as a part of any month.

2. The calendar of moonlight, developed from a more primitive calendar about 2000 B.C. A lunar plan, not a solar one. Many adjustments needed in the handling.

3. The calendar of the seven-day week, perfected about 1500 B.C. and ascribed to Moses. A solar plan of great mathematical simplicity. The beginning of the year was set at the time of the autumn equinox, the year being divided into 52 weeks. The extra day, or two on leap years, was not counted as a part of a week.

I I I

Today's Calendar;
Its Background and
Modifications

ALL OF THE GREAT CALENDAR PLANS *of the ancient world of the eastern Mediterranean are represented, at least to some degree, in the calendar that is ours today. The oddity is that a calendar built from such variant approaches to the measurement of time should actually be workable.*

The Zodiac: Gemini

7

JULIUS CAESAR'S
CALENDAR FOR THE
ROMAN WORLD

About the year 1000 b.c., restless tribal groups stirred in southern Europe. A sharp change of climate may have been responsible. Within a century or two many tribes seemed suddenly possessed by an overwhelming desire for new pastures for their flocks or new homes for their people. Some of these tribes were being displaced by those behind them, others were reaching for less crowded lands or more fertile soils.

The Italians were among these tribes. Coming into Italy from the northeast they reached the rough hill country of the central mountain range. In secluded valleys they found pasture grasses for their flocks and fertile soil for their small farms.

A few centuries later, a wave of outsiders called Etruscans swept into Italy from the sea. Coming probably from Asia Minor, the newcomers were in well-organized groups. They stayed away from the mountains, selecting the broad valley of the Po River at the north and the coastal lands on the west side of Italy to the north of the Tiber River. These people were made up largely of businessmen, not farmers. They had large estates, handled by slave labor. Their leaders thought in terms of aqueducts, chariot races, and the laying out of broad highways. Like other businessmen of that time and this, they loved rich food, then built marble-lined public baths and gymnasiums with which to keep their weight down.

The Rise of Rome

THE LAND OF THE ETRUSCANS, which is the modern Italian province of Tuscany, bordered ancient Latium. The only crossing point was a fording place on the Tiber River. A crude bridge was built, and then a fortress. Its name: Rome.

It is doubtful if the Etruscans ever made a full-scale effort to push the Romans from their bridge and overrun Latium. A land so poor was scarcely worth taking. But the Romans never relaxed their vigilance. And they harassed the Etruscans with quick raids across the river.

Julius Caesar's Calendar

After three centuries the situation changed. The fortress gates were thrown wide, the Roman legions marched through to annihilate the Etruscan cities one by one. By the close of the following century those legions would be masters of all Italy and their leaders would be looking for more lands to conquer.

Early Rome, and Calendar Handling

IN THE BEGINNING OF ROMAN HISTORY the direct contacts between the rich, cultured Etruscans and the rustic men of Latium must have been few. Yet the Romans secured from the Etruscans an alphabet, a number system, a way for surveying land and measuring distances, and a calendar. The Etruscans had not invented any of these things but had brought them from Asia Minor—or wherever they had come from when they sailed to Italy. Their calendar was the calendar of moonlight.

According to Roman legend the fortress city by the Tiber bridge was founded in 753 B.C. In the year 47 B.C. Julius Caesar substituted a new calendar plan for the earlier one, which had been in use for seven centuries, though not always in exactly the same form. Roman writers of later decades—Ovid, Plutarch, and Livy—have supplied some facts about the probable nature of the calendar in the earlier centuries. But their "facts" can be questioned. According to Alexander Philip, an English scholar, "Notwithstanding the antiquity and authority of the writers who furnish the [early-calendar] account, it is probably very largely conjectural." Philip is more definite about the calendar period after the Greek system had become a part of the Roman plan, though somewhat mishandled. "A somewhat irregular group of calendar [adjustments] was still required, and being in the hands of the Pontifices, whose methods and reasons were kept strictly secret, negligence, ignorance, and still more—corruption, led to great irregularities and a resulting dislocation and uncertainty in the Roman calendar."[1]

To explain the major difficulties that the Romans encountered in the early calendar building, we may *suppose* that the country people of Latium did not use the calendar of moonlight and that the men of Rome did. (You are warned that this is conjecture.) It is known that the Roman farm year started in spring, running through the times of planting and of the harvest, back to spring again. It is known that twelve months were used, that these were numbered at first, and that later half of them received special names instead of the names by the numbering plan. Since these months maintained a fixed position in the year's calendar they did not correspond to the months of the calendar of moonlight, which move, there being sometimes 12 new moons and sometimes 13 new moons in a year.

The calendar plan adopted for the military purposes of Rome was evidently that of the calendar of moonlight. At first the handling was quite elementary.

[1] Philip, Alexander *The Calendar* Cambridge University Press, 1921. Pages 11, 12.

Julius Caesar's Calendar

Watchers noted each month the first appearance of the new crescent moon in the western sky. In time, the date of appearance could be predicted, and the predictions checked by observations. The Etruscans were to pass on the idea of using 30 days and 29 days for alternate months, the insertion of one "leap" day every 32 months, and of one less "leap" day every 800 months.

As the soldiers of early Rome were drawn from the small farms of Latium, they tended to use the farmers' calendar, blending with it the soldiers' calendar. The greatest difficulty must have been in connection with the year. After the Romans conquered Greece they found that the Greeks were keeping their lunar year in line with the solar year by counting some years as 12 lunar months and others as 13 lunar months. Numerous adjustments had to be made in the handling, and the Roman officials in charge of the calendar apparently tried to make them correctly when the Greek plan was adopted. In a century, however, the Roman year slipped out of position, for blunders had been made in the adjustments. (This last part of the calendar story is fact, not conjecture.)

Julius Caesar and the Calendar

IN THE YEAR 63 B.C. Julius Caesar became Pontifex Maximus, or chief of the Pontifices, apparently at his own request. At that time he was already noted for his military accomplishments and his organizational skill but was not yet supreme commander of the Roman armies. He took his new duties seriously and made some relatively minor calendar changes. Seventeen years later, as Pontifex Maximus, supreme commander of the armies, and, in addition, Roman Dictator, he announced the establishment of *a new Roman calendar* to replace the old one.

The new calendar was a modified form of the calendar of Thoth. Caesar had studied this calendar of Egypt during his Egyptian military campaign, in which he established Cleopatra on the throne. To him the simplicity was remarkable. Although Egyptian temple priests looked after the handling of the calendar, no actual supervision was normally required. The sole correction needed was the addition of a single day at the end of the year every fourth year. (Actually, this extra leap-year day needed to be left out every 125 years to keep the calendar in *exact* agreement with the year.)

The months of this plan did not match those of moonlight. Each of the 12 months had the same number of days, 30. For market-day purposes the month was divided into 10-day groups. So neither the months nor the market-day times required any supervision at all.

To Caesar the simplicity must have appeared broken by the Egyptian manner of handling the extra 5 or 6 days at the year's end. These days were not counted in business transactions and were not allotted to any month. (We can suppose that the businessmen of Alexandria found the situation awkward.)

Caesar went over the Egyptian calendar plan quite

fully with Sosigenes, an eminent astronomer of Alexandria. At the close of the Egyptian military campaign he took the astronomer to Rome as a consultant in the building of the new calendar for the Roman world.

Details of Caesar's Calendar Plan

THE NEW CALENDAR DID NOT COPY that of Egypt. The chief difference was in the handling of the 5 or 6 extra days that Thoth had bunched at the end of the calendar year and had not counted as belonging to any month or considered as being counted in the year's transactions. Caesar divided these days among the months. Since 6 days, the number in each leap year, is just half of 12, the number of months, he spread the six days among the 12 months by giving one day to alternate months. He counted March as the first month of the year because that was traditional in the old Roman calendar. So March received the first of the extra days, giving it a length of 31 days. From that point the rest of the odd-numbered months received extra days, each having, as a result, a total of 31 days. The six even-numbered months kept the 30-day length of Thoth's months. February was the last of the even-numbered months. Its length was 30 days, but only on a leap year. In an ordinary year there would be 5, not 6, extra days to be distributed. February, at the year's end, dropped to 29 days in those years. (You may be puzzled. February is not handled in that way today. But that is the way it was in Caesar's plan.)

After a year of preparation, the new calendar went

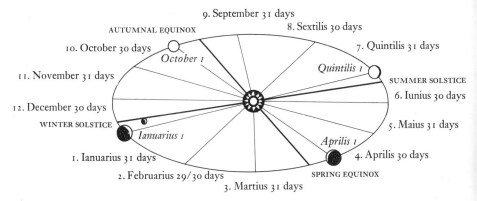

Ianuarius 1. Year begins (46 B.C.) at the time of the
first new moon following the winter solstice.

into effect at the time of the first new moon after the winter solstice of the year that we know as 46 B.C. It is not known why the time of the winter solstice was chosen. The Roman year had previously begun near the spring equinox, and Thoth's year had begun at the autumn equinox. The use of the new moon as a starting time may have been a concession to the ages-old idea that the new moon was the proper starting time for any month. But the result was a year that started at the first of January, ten days after the winter solstice. The fourth month, April, would be starting, then, about ten days after the spring equinox; the seventh month, July, about ten days after the summer solstice; the tenth month, October, about ten days after the autumn equinox.

Although the time of the year's beginning was changed from March to January, the names of the months were not changed by Caesar's handling. As half of the months had been numbered from March as a starting month, their number names would no longer indicate the month's location for the year starting with January. Here, in table form, is the *old listing:*

1. Martius (March)	7. September (seventh)
2. Aprilis (April)	8. October (eighth)
3. Maius (May)	9. November (ninth)
4. Iunius (June)	10. December (tenth)
5. Quintilis (fifth)	11. Ianuarius (January)
6. Sextilis (sixth)	12. Februarius (February)

Julius Caesar's Calendar

Table 1 shows the plan used by Caesar in spreading out the 6 or 5 extra days, as well as the numbering of the months under *his plan*.

TABLE 1

CAESAR'S ARRANGEMENT OF THE ROMAN CALENDAR

Showing how the extra days of the Egyptian calendar were spread among the twelve months

MONTH	IAN.	FEB.	MAR.	APR.	MAI
number	1	2	3	4	5
Days added to 30 *in the spreading*	1		1		1
TOTAL FOR MONTH	31	29;30*	31	30	31

IUN.	QUI.	SEX.	SEP.	OCT.	NOV.	DEC.
6	7	8	9	10	11	12
	1		1		1	
30	31	30	31	30	31	30

* Ordinary year; leap year.

In 44 B.C. after two years of operation of the new calendar, the name of the month Quintilis was changed to Julius (July) to honor the name of Julius Caesar, who had been assassinated a short time before.

TABLE 2

THE ROMAN CALENDAR ARRANGEMENT AFTER THE TIME OF AUGUSTUS

MONTH	JAN.	FEB.	MAR.	APR.	MAY
number	1	2	3	4	5
Days by Caesar's arrangement	31	29;30*	31	30	31
Modified arrangement under Augustus	31	28;29*	31	30	31

JUN.	JUL.	AUG.	SEP.	OCT.	NOV.	DEC.
6	7	8	9	10	11	12
30	31	30	31	30	31	30
30	31	31	30	31	30	31

* Ordinary year; leap year.

Calendar Modifications Under the Emperor Augustus

Augustus followed Julius Caesar as the first emperor of the Roman Empire. In the year 8 B.C., during his reign, a second month name was changed. By order of the Roman Senate, the month of Sextilis was renamed Augustus (August) in honor of the Emperor. Along with the name change the month's length was changed from 30 to 31 days, by taking a day from February. For the four months following August the added days were shifted along as shown in Table 2.

The Zodiac: Cancer

8

THE ENLARGEMENT OF
THE ROMAN CALENDAR
UNDER CONSTANTINE

Among the Romans, market days were set as close as possible to intervals of one quarter of a month. In the 30-day months of the calendar of moonlight the intervals separating market days ran 8, 7, 8, and 7 days. For the 29-day months the division was 8, 7, 7, and 7 days. Under the new plan of the year, the 28-day February was divided into 7, 7, 7, and 7 market-day intervals; the 29-day February of a leap year was divided into 8, 7, 7, and 7 market-day intervals; the four 30-day months were divided, as before, into 8, 7,

8, and 7 intervals; the seven 31-day months were given intervals of 8, 8, 8, and 7 days. Thus by either the older calendar plan or the new one the market days were either 7 or 8 days apart.

Constantine and the Seven-Day Week

FOR THE FIRST THREE CENTURIES after the Roman calendar of Caesar was adopted these varying intervals between market days continued. Then in A.D. 321 a change was made that would eliminate the 8-day market-day interval, leaving only the 7-day interval. Emperor Constantine had, earlier, announced his conversion to Christianity. In that year he signed an act making the seven-day week of the Christians *legal* throughout the Roman world. When Christianity became the state religion of the Empire the use of the seven-day week became universal. And when Christian missionaries went out from Rome to convert the Goths and Anglo-Saxons of western Europe the seven-day week went along.

The plan of the seven-day week had been taken over by the Christians from the Jews. The Jews of that period were not adhering to the calendar of Moses in one important respect. The one day, or two days in leap years, that came at the year's end had not been counted as days of the week in the original handling. As a result, both the year and each of the four seasons began on the first day of the week and ended on the last day of the week, and each season had the same number of Sabbaths. The Jews later modified this system by making the special day or days a part of the week. The year that had begun by the old plan on the first day of the week and ended on the last day of the week, year after year, now could start one year on the first day of the week, the next year on the second day of the week, the third year on the third day of the week, and so on for common years. After a leap year the starting day jumped over a week day; the third-day beginning of that year, for example, would be followed by a fifth-day beginning for the next year. (It was from this leaping-over of a week day that leap year got its name.)

The Zodiac: Leo

9

THE

CALENDAR CORRECTION

OF GREGORY

THE EGYPTIAN PRIESTS, in their thousands of years of record keeping, had discovered that one leap-year day needed to be omitted every 125 years. The explanation is that the true length of the year is 365.2422 days instead of 365.25 days, the year's length around which the calendar had been built. The difference between the two values is only 11 minutes 14 seconds a year, but in 125 years that difference amounts to a whole day.

We may suppose that Caesar was not told about

this essential omission by Sosigenes, the astronomer. Or perhaps it was considered unimportant. Yet in 1,000 years the error would amount to 8 days.

The Gregorian Adjustment

IN A.D. 325 an important Church Council was held in the city of Nicaea in Asia Minor. One topic under discussion had to do with the time of the spring equinox as related to the observance of Easter. A Church Council held at Trent in Italy *1,220 years later* had the time of the spring equinox again under discussion. The equinox of 325 had come on March 21; 1,257 years later, the equinox for 1582 came on March 11. In those intervening years the calendar had developed an error of 10 days.

Some corrective action was called for. After extensive discussion of possible remedies, Pope Gregory III promulgated the following order, now referred to as the *Gregorian Adjustment*.

In order to maintain in future a more exact correspondence, three out of every four years of an even century length shall be common years instead of leap years. Those years of even century length which are divisible by 400 without remainder shall be retained as leap years. [The result was the same as omitting a leap year every 125 years. The error remaining would be only one day in about 3,000 years.]

To correct the calendar and eliminate the ten-day error that had developed, Gregory announced that the calendar was to. be rectified by taking out those ten days. When the program was put into effect in October, 1582, the date of *October 4 was to be followed the next day by October 15*. Some confusion resulted. Servants hired by the month or artisans by the half year complained bitterly over "the ten days lost out of their life." They insisted upon being paid for them. The landlords and shop keepers refused to pay for work that was not done. No one was happy.

Some Birthday Information

THE GREGORIAN ADJUSTMENT was not put into effect in Great Britain and her American colonies until 1752. Since the year 1700 was a leap year by the Roman calendar of Caesar but not by the adjusted plan, there were by 1752 *eleven days* to be taken off in making the change. *The day following September 2 of that year was put down as September 14*. Opportunity was taken at the same time to adjust the beginning of the year from March 24, which had been used as New Year's Eve in England and the Colonies, to January 1, the time of the year's beginning in the other countries of Western Europe.

We have at this point a birthday record to examine. George Washington was a young man when the calendar change was made. According to the reference books of today he was born February 22, 1732. By his family records his birthday was February 11, 1732. Both are right. He called the first his birthday New Style, the other his birthday Old Style.

Benjamin Franklin "lost the eleven days out of life" when he was forty-six. Shortly before the date at which the Act would go into effect he wrote half-jokingly in his *Almanack:*[1]

Be not astonished, nor look with scorn, dear reader, at such a deduction of days, nor regret as for the loss of so much time, but take this for your consolation, that your expenses will appear lighter and your mind be more at ease. And what an indulgence is here, for those who love their pillow to lie down in Peace on the second of this month and not perhaps awake till the morning of the fourteenth.

That was how it happened that Colonial America, like the entire English world, had no history for eleven calendar days—days that were "gone with the wind."

[1] Quoted by Cowan, H. C., *Time and Its Measurement*, World Publishing Company, New York, 1958, page 29.

The Zodiac: Virgo

1 0

THE PLACE OF

EASTER AND CHRISTMAS

IN THE CALENDAR

The Story Behind Easter and Its Variable Date

Down through the ages, almost every nation has celebrated a springtime festival. In the case of Moses and the Israelites this festival took on an extra religious fervor, for on such a spring night when the moon was at its full they had slipped out of Egypt on their way to a promised land. In memory of that night of deliverance, they celebrated this day of the *Passover* as the greatest festival of the year.

The English word *Easter* is the old Norse name for the divinity of spring—the gay spirit that brought greenness to the hills, that sent the fish up the streams to their breeding grounds, that made the colts race across the fields, and filled the valleys with warm, balmy air. Easter in the north countries had been the greatest festival of the year.

Christianity took over the Passover time but turned the religious nature of the old celebration into the Christian message of the Resurrection. Then when Christian missionaries moved northward through western Europe the newer religious festival of the Church was blended with the old spring celebration under the old name of Easter.

The important Church Council of Nicaea, already mentioned, decided that the spring festival was to be celebrated on the same date throughout the Christian world. That date, changing from year to year, was to be the first Sunday after the first full moon after the spring equinox. Sometimes this first full moon of spring appeared at a time close to the equinox, sometimes at a time almost a lunar month beyond the equinox. But Easter's date is never the same for any two years in succession, for that is true of the moon's timing.

The Christmas Season

THE BACKGROUND FOR THE CELEBRATION of Christmas is quite different from that for Easter. This festival time came at, or near, the winter solstice—at about the time when the winter days start, slowly, to increase in length, while the winter nights, just as slowly, start to become shorter. In all north Europe in the long winter period, cold grips the fields and the hills, ice blocks the water passageways. The snow-bound houses are shuttered tightly against the north winds. Life goes on, but in a subdued way. Then, with the solstice, the morning light gradually grows stronger. Hope can fill the minds and hearts—hope of a pleasant and prosperous new year.

Every Northland country had its own way of celebrating the winter-solstice time. For five days or longer, neighbors would congregate. At times with almost forced gaiety, at times with real joy in the accomplishments of the year that had passed and with hope for the year ahead, these neighbors met. The celebrations were as distinctive as the people themselves. The Yule log of Britain, the fir tree of Saxony, the mistletoe, the plum pudding, the toasted chestnuts— all had their part in the gaiety of the drawn-out cele-bration.

In Holland, Belgium, France, and certain other countries, a somewhat earlier celebration was put on for the children. With Saint Nicholas, or Santa Claus, as a patron character, this one-day celebration involved the giving of simple gifts to the children and nuts and candies for all the family.

Christmas Day

MOST OF THE FORMS of celebration men-tioned were for the family and the community. They were not given a religious presentation. After the in-troduction of Christianity, the Church selected one day of the season as a special day. This was the day of Christmas, set on December 25. It stressed the story of the birth of the Christ child and the dramatization of the events of that birth.

The Christmas season was, then, a composite of events centered around the time of the winter solstice that reflected the glorying of people in the return of sunshine and warmth to a wintry world, and the joy of family life.

The Zodiac: Libra

I I

THE PRESENT CALENDAR;

AND A POSSIBLE ONE

FOR THE FUTURE

N O MAJOR CHANGE has been made in the calendar used in western Europe and the Americas—that is, in *our* calendar—since the adoption of the adjusted calendar form of Gregory. This calendar is a composite of two unlike time divisions of the year, one built about the month, the other about the seven-day week. Over the centuries neither of these independent plans gained such pre-eminence over the other as to cause the lesser one to be abandoned.

Names for the Days of the Week

ONE FEATURE of the week plan has not been mentioned. It relates to the names used for the seven week days. This naming uses an old five-day "week," to which two names were added by the Christian missionaries to make up a Christian week of seven days. The five-day "week" had been brought to England from across the North Sea by the Angles and the Saxons about A.D. 400. Several centuries later the seven-day week was introduced by the missionaries.

The Anglo-Saxon days were named for the important deities common among all Norse, Gothic, and Germanic groups.

Tiwsday or Tuesday—the day of the god Tiw
Wodensday or Wednesday—the day of the god Woden
Thorsday or Thursday—the day of the god Thunor or Thor
Frigsday or Friday—the day of the goddess Frig
Seternesday or Saturday—the day of the god Seterne

The two days added by the missionaries were:

Sunday—the day of the sun
Monday—the day of the moon.

The Anglo-Saxon names matched in nature and order those of the Egyptian deities whose names were used by Thoth for his five "extra" days at the year's end. They also matched the names of deities that the Chaldeans gave to those same five days of the calendar they adopted from Egypt. About two thousand years after that adoption in Chaldea the astronomers of Babylon assigned these same deity names to the five planets that they had been studying. Greek astronomers, using the Babylonian naming plan for the planets, substituted the names of important Greek deities for those of Chaldea and Babylonia. The Roman astronomers copied the Greek idea but introduced the names of their own important deities. For convenience in comparing the various lists of deities, those of the Egyptians, Chaldeans, Romans, and Anglo-Saxons are put down:

Egypt—Osiris, Horus, Set, the goddess Isis, Nephthys

Chaldea—Nergal, Nabu, Marduk, the goddess Ishtar, Ninib

Rome—Mars, Mercury, Jupiter, the goddess Venus, Saturn

Anglo-Saxon—Tiw, Woden, Thor, the goddess Frig, Seterne.

A Probable Explanation for the Anglo-Saxon Naming

THE LISTS OF MATCHING NAMES might be explained by assuming (1) that the religions represented were essentially identical and had a common origin, or (2) that the similarity came from the uniform handling of Thoth's calendar plan in the several countries. Neither of these suggestions is acceptable. The various religions were not comparable. Greece and Rome had not used the Thoth calendar. There is a further possibility: the similarity in the case of the Anglo-Saxons might be due to a direct transference of the Thoth calendar to north-central Europe at an early historical time. There need be no connection of the day names with the planet names.

Two groups of facts support the assumption that the calendar came directly from Egypt to north-central Europe. Recent work on weight and measure systems has given convincing evidence that the Egyptian decimal systems of length, farm areas, capacity sizes, and weights reached north-central Europe with Phoenicians trading at Black Sea ports about 1000 B.C.[1]

In translating and interpreting the Norse *Skalds Kaparmal*, written about A.D. 63, the Frenchman Paul Du Chaillu was able to reconstruct the Norseman's calendar. It contained 12 months of 30 days each. The month was divided into three periods of 10 days each.

[1] For details see the author's *The Romance of Weights and Measures*, 1960, chapter 2.

At the summer's end was a group of 5 days that was not counted as a part of any month. Apparently the 5-day naming plan was used only with these particular days.[1] The plan was evidently that of Thoth except that the year began in midwinter rather than in autumn.

AT THIS POINT we leave the story of the development of the calendar to indicate some efforts that were made in the past century or so toward improving some undesirable features of the present-day calendar.

Comte's Calendar Ideas

IN 1849, AUGUSTE COMTE OF FRANCE proposed that the calendar of the months be discontinued in favor of an improved form of the seven-day week calendar. Without knowing that he was doing so, he had rebuilt the basic seven-day week plan of Moses, devised about thirty-four centuries before. He announced that the last day of each common year and the last two days of a leap year were to be set aside as days of celebration and not counted as week days. In this simple handling all years would have fifty-two weeks. The year, and each of the four seasons of the year, could start on the first day of the week and end on the last day of the week, so all seasons would have

[1] Paul Du Chaillu, *The Viking Age*, 1886, chapter 4, pages 37-38.

the same number of Sundays, and thirty day months.

In his enthusiasm he went beyond the plan of Moses. He divided the year into months of 4 weeks or 28 days each. The result was a year of 13 months. He would substitute these months of even length for the months of the Roman calendar with their confusing differences of length.

Moses had most certainly been aware of the possibility of dividing the year into periods of 28 days each and thus of creating years of exactly 13 months. At various times in history, tradesmen had set up such an arrangement. But the disadvantage of such a simple division of the year was that it interfered with equal seasons of 91 days (13 weeks) each. That number of days would be equal to 3¼ 28-day months.

A Suggested Modification for the Calendar Months

A SEPARATE ATTEMPT to simplify the calendar was started in 1887. Its purpose was to make the four seasons of 91 days each exactly equal to three months each. In the Roman calendar the three months that include February are shorter than the three months that include August, and the half year from January up to July is shorter than the other half. Why not remedy this unevenness by having each season consist of one 31-day month and two 30-day months? Actually, very few changes would be needed if the proposed handling were put into effect. Many people were interested.

The "World Calendar" Proposal

BY 1930 A NEW CALENDAR was formulated. The present calendar was modified by the insertion of a day in the common year and two days in a leap year, to be days of no week and no month. One of these days of no week and no month was placed at the end of the year, the other at the end of the half year. Also the plan required a month of 31 days to be followed by two months of 30 days each in every season. It was sponsored by the World Calendar Association, whose membership included people from all the countries of Western Europe and the Americas.

In 1956 this calendar was presented to the United Nations for adoption as a calendar for the entire world. The reaction was unfavorable. It was not approved by the committee of that organization to which it was assigned, so was not discussed on the floor of the Assembly. At some future time the calendar plan may, possibly, be presented again.

THE WORLD CALENDAR

FIRST QUARTER

	S	M	T	W	T	F	S
JAN	1	2	3	4	5	6	7
	8	9	10	11	12	13	14
	15	16	17	18	19	20	21
	22	23	24	25	26	27	28
	29	30	31				
FEB				1	2	3	4
	5	6	7	8	9	10	11
	12	13	14	15	16	17	18
	19	20	21	22	23	24	25
	26	27	28	29	30		
MAR						1	2
	3	4	5	6	7	8	9
	10	11	12	13	14	15	16
	17	18	19	20	21	22	23
	24	25	26	27	28	29	30

THIRD QUARTER

	S	M	T	W	T	F	S
JUL	1	2	3	4	5	6	7
	8	9	10	11	12	13	14
	15	16	17	18	19	20	21
	22	23	24	25	26	27	28
	29	30	31				
AUG				1	2	3	4
	5	6	7	8	9	10	11
	12	13	14	15	16	17	18
	19	20	21	22	23	24	25
	26	27	28	29	30		
SEP						1	2
	3	4	5	6	7	8	9
	10	11	12	13	14	15	16
	17	18	19	20	21	22	23
	24	25	26	27	28	29	30

SECOND QUARTER

	S	M	T	W	T	F	S
APR	1	2	3	4	5	6	7
	8	9	10	11	12	13	14
	15	16	17	18	19	20	21
	22	23	24	25	26	27	28
	29	30	31				
MAY				1	2	3	4
	5	6	7	8	9	10	11
	12	13	14	15	16	17	18
	19	20	21	22	23	24	25
	26	27	28	29	30		
JUN						1	2
	3	4	5	6	7	8	9
	10	11	12	13	14	15	16
	17	18	19	20	21	22	23
	24	25	26	27	28	29	30 **

FOURTH QUARTER

	S	M	T	W	T	F	S
OCT	1	2	3	4	5	6	7
	8	9	10	11	12	13	14
	15	16	17	18	19	20	21
	22	23	24	25	26	27	28
	29	30	31				
NOV				1	2	3	4
	5	6	7	8	9	10	11
	12	13	14	15	16	17	18
	19	20	21	22	23	24	25
	26	27	28	29	30		
DEC						1	2
	3	4	5	6	7	8	9
	10	11	12	13	14	15	16
	17	18	19	20	21	22	23
	24	25	26	27	28	29	30 *

**LEAP-YEAR DAY, follows
June 30 in leap years.

*YEAR-END DAY, follows
December 30 every year.

Up to this point this book has been a record of people who developed a calendar of some kind with which to keep track of the passage of time.

The remaining portion is in the nature of a supplement to that earlier part. The first of two sections relates to methods that have been used for the backward extension of calendar timing to give dates for events before recorded history. The final section broadens the calendar handling to take in variations of the seasons in nature, from year to year.

I V

Backward Extension
of the Calendar Plan:

METHODS, OLD AND NEW,

FOR DATING THE EVENTS

OF EARLY HISTORY

THE KNOWLEDGE OF HUMAN EXISTENCE *goes back
in time far beyond the written records. Knowledge
of dates in the long-ago past could act as keys to
early history. Rapid progress is being made toward
determining such dates, using methods old and new.
Some of these will be presented.*

The Zodiac: Scorpius

12

SOLVING BY ASTRONOMY

THE RIDDLE OF

SOME EARLY DATES

I N ANCIENT EGYPT the history of long-ago centuries can be followed through hieroglyphic writing and pictures on the walls of temples and tombs. Except for the confused period of about a century and a half when the Hyksos kings robbed temples and destroyed records, the general story of the kings, dynasties, and kingdoms of ancient Egypt can be considered quite complete. But no calendar dates are available for the early centuries. In an indirect way the skill of the modern astronomer has, however, been able to fill in certain dates of historical importance.

A Calendar Date for Khufu

MENES THE MIGHTY was the founder of the first dynasty in Egypt. He is almost wholly a legendary figure because his exploits came before hieroglyphic writing was developed. Khufu, the builder of the Great Pyramid, was the first king of the fourth dynasty. In the several centuries between his time and that of Menes, enormous advances had been made in measurement, surveying, and engineering. Some advances had also been made in astronomy. Khufu, his mind full of big ideas, had a "telescope" built into the great stone structure while it was under construction. As mentioned on page 34, this first of all large telescopes was immovable and carried no lenses or other equipment as a modern large instrument would. It was merely a long straight tubelike passageway that started at the king's funeral chamber, deep in the heart of the great tomb. It slanted toward a small opening in the north face of the pyramid and was evidently aimed at the north star. Each night as Khufu would peer through his telescope when the pyramid was under construction, the star would come into view, move across the opening, then disappear. This was to happen night after night, month after month, year after year. To one standing on the ground looking at the night sky, all other stars seemed to swing around this central star. Those in star constellations farthest from the north star would, in their swinging, move in and out of sight across the horizon as the various seasons passed.

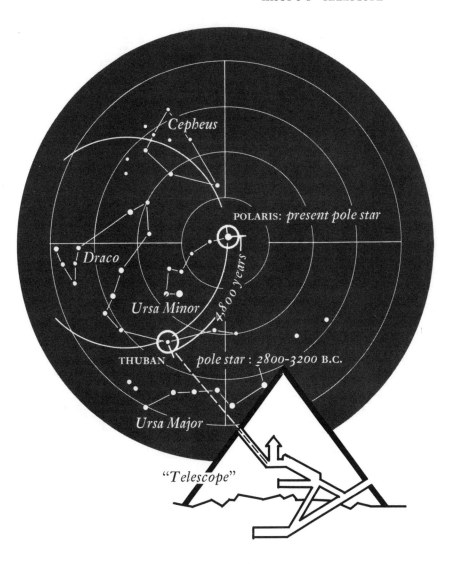

Cepheus

POLARIS: *present pole star*

Draco

4,800 years

Ursa Minor

THUBAN   *pole star : 2800-3200 B.C.*

Ursa Major

"Telescope"

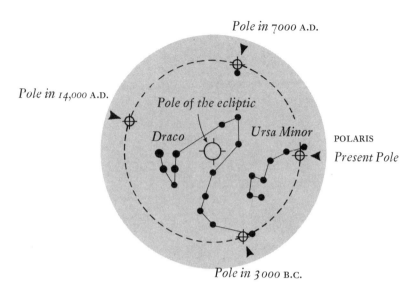

Pole in 7000 A.D.

Pole in 14,000 A.D.

Pole of the ecliptic

Draco

Ursa Minor

POLARIS
Present Pole

Pole in 3000 B.C.

Path of the Celestial Pole,
a complete cycle requiring 26,000 years

THE EARTH'S PRECESSIONAL MOTION AND THE MIGRATING POLE

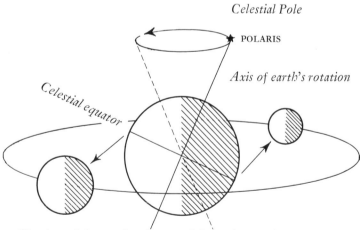

Celestial Pole

POLARIS

Axis of earth's rotation

Celestial equator

The plane of the moon's orbit around the earth approximates
the plane of the earth's orbit around the sun. The moon's attraction on
the bulging equator of the tilted earth seeks to bring it "upright." The
effect is to cause the earth's axis to describe a slow circle against the
background of the heavens, each cycle taking 26,000 years.

According to the wording used in present-day astronomies, Khufu's telescope was aimed at the Celestial Pole, or the place where the axis of the spinning earth would, if extended, pass out into space. Today that axis passes one degree from Polaris, our north star. Each night this star, for us, swings through a tiny circle as it seems to move with the rest of the sky about the Celestial Pole.

But Polaris, so the astronomers say, has been the pole star for only a few hundred years. The axis of the spinning earth has a slow sideways motion and the Celestial Pole goes along. They report that in the time of Columbus the earth's axis was pointing $3\frac{1}{2}$ degrees away from Polaris. For the days that lie ahead, they predict that by the year 2100 the axis will point within half a degree of Polaris. Then it will shift away. The next *bright* star to come close to the Pole will be Alpha Cephei, in about 7500.

Returning to Khufu and his telescope of about five thousand years ago, we can be quite certain that he was watching as his pole star a bright star that would be at some distance from the present location of the Celestial Pole. To turn the problem backward, if we but knew *what star* he was seeing through his telescope we could find, with the assistance of the astronomer, the time when the pyramid was being built. His telescope was aimed about $3\frac{1}{2}$ degrees below the Pole, not directly at it, so the "mystery pole star" was evidently moving through a tiny circle. As seen through the telescope the star would appear, then disappear, doing this regularly each night throughout the entire year.

The astronomers of today, after making numerous calculations, believe that he was looking at Thuban, a bright star which is now about halfway between the middle star in the handle of the Great Dipper and the two stars at the end of the bowl of the Little Dipper. Thuban was closest to the Celestial Pole about 3000 B.C. But in that position it could not have been seen by Khufu because of the way his telescope was aimed. Had he been looking seven centuries earlier or later than 3000 B.C., the star would have passed squarely across the center of the opening. Two centuries from that date the star would have been seen clearly each night but not at the center of the telescope opening. Thus by either 3200 or 2800 B.C. it would have moved in and out of sight for anyone peering through the telescope. Not knowing any details as to how Khufu saw the star, astronomers have had to do some guessing. One commonly held belief is that the Great Pyramid was built about the year 2800 B.C., or two centuries less than 5,000 years ago. This choice over 3200 B.C. was on historical grounds.

A Dating for Early Chaldean History

KHUFU WATCHED THE POLE STAR; the early astronomers of Chaldea watched the constellations. They knew, for example, that the bright star Aldebaran stayed out of sight below the horizon for a part of the year. After long periods of observation they found that it was possible to predict with certainty when this star would reappear above the rim of the horizon. They made a record of the date of this event which happened every year at the same time of the year.

This bright star no longer rises on the day that it did in ancient Chaldea. There is a difference in the rising time of two months nine days. This change, like the shift in the pole star, results from the slow movement of the Celestial Pole. It follows a circular path that takes about 26,000 years to complete. So we may be sure that in 26,000 years after Khufu looked through his telescope the star Thuban will be back as the pole star. And 26,000 years after the Chaldeans recorded the date of Aldebaran's rising that star will be rising again on approximately the same date of the year. The astronomers, using this knowledge, have calculated how long ago the observations were made in old Chaldea. Taking the fractional part of the year shown by two months nine days and multiplying this fraction by 26,000 years gave close to 5,000 years. That number of years gave a date of about 3000 B.C., or slightly after the probable date for the erection of the Great Pyramid.

A Date for the Stone Lion of Commagene

THESE TIMING METHODS of the astronomer do not give a precise dating. The fault lies not in the method but in the vagueness of the facts reported about the stars. In the case about to be described the information offered was adequate and the use of the information gave a precise time prediction.

A few years ago archeologists visited Commagene,

a small ancient kingdom on the narrow upper reaches of the Euphrates just before the river flows into the wide arid valley. Today this area is a treeless, unpopulated wasteland, the fertility of its soil lost by drouth and erosion. But two thousand years ago it was noted for its timber, well-fed cattle, and bountiful grain. In fact, it has been recorded that Commagene was the richest small kingdom taken over by the Romans in the formation of the Roman Empire.

This kingdom was at the height of its prosperity in the general period between the conquest of Persia by

Alexander the Great and the coming of the Romans under Aurelian six centuries later. For its defense a flat-topped hill on the mountainous side of the country was turned into a citadel. A strong stone wall enclosed the citadel area. The approach to the high ground followed an easily defended roadway. In the reign of King Antiochus statues of both Greek and Persian deities had evidently been placed at the east and west sides of the citadel, the king having a statue of himself added to the others. Near the entrance a lion figure, sculptured in relief, had been set. Nineteen stars in recognizable constellations were scattered on or near the lion's body. A crescent moon appeared on the breast. In addition, three planets were shown in a peculiar "conjunction," or position relative to each other. Each planet was identified by the initial letter of its name in Greek. In the wording we use, they were Jupiter, Mercury, and Mars.

When recent archeologists reached the old land of Commagene they found that earthquakes had destroyed portions of the citadel wall, toppled the row of statues, and left the lion in large fragments. Neither Alexandrian nor Roman history mentioned the name of Antiochus. It seemed impossible to give a date to the time of his reign, for at first it was not recognized that the lion design was the work of an astronomer and would tell, in an astronomer's way, the date of erection. But Professor Otto Neugebauer of Brown University sensed the significance of the design and set out to determine the date. He realized that the date was after the time of Alexander (from the Greek marking of the planets) and before the time of Aurelian (for the Kingdom of Commagene was still in existence). He noted that the stars were arranged within the constellations differently from the way they are today. This shifting of star positions comes from the fact that the stars, though seemingly motionless, are in motion. So, by a study of the nineteen stars in relation to other stars, he narrowed the possible time of erection to a mere portion of a century. The conjunctions of the three planets come so infrequently but can be predicted by the astronomer with such great accuracy that the time of erection could be narrowed to a particular season. Finally the crescent moon on the lion's chest was the clue to the particular day. His answer was July 7, 61 B.C.[1]

[1] "Throne Above the Euphrates" by Theresa Goell, *National Geographic* Magazine, March, 1961, pages 390-405.

Ursa Major

I 3

USING CARBON, THE

CHEMICAL ELEMENT,

AS A REVERSE-ACTING

CLOCK OF TIME

BACK BEYOND THE DAYS OF PYRAMID BUILDING and star watching, back beyond the time of calendar designing and hieroglyphic writing, lies an almost uncharted expanse of human existence that has remained until recently largely without even an approximate time schedule. We shall start the discussion of how a very modern dating plan was able to do what had never been done before, by going back to the closing days of the Ice Ages.

At the Close of the Ice Ages

THAT STRANGE PERIOD of earth's history, the Ice Ages, came to a close about 10,000 years ago. In the centuries before, more snow had been falling each year in North America and Europe than could be melted in the days of summer. In time the steadily accumulating snow formed deep beds of glacial ice. Century after century the snow fell, building the glacial ice up to *two miles in depth*.

With the retreat of the glaciers, life flowed back. Hardy tundra moss followed the glaciers closely. Firs, pines, and spruces were not far behind. As the climate grew milder, oak and beech forests displaced the firs. Grasslands appeared among the oak forests. Animals moved in. And man, the hunter, moved in too.

With the changing shorelines of ocean, sea, and bay, and the slow warming of northern waters, most of the fish made shifts in their feeding grounds, some of them frequently. And man, the fisherman, changed his implements and fishing locations to handle the shifts made by the fish.

In southwestern Asia man domesticated animals and invented farming seven thousand years ago. This agricultural explosion *may* have reached central Europe about three thousand years ago. If so, the Ice Age had passed about seven thousand years or more before. Until recently there seemed no certainty about such time values for these events, though several methods had been used with a measure of success.

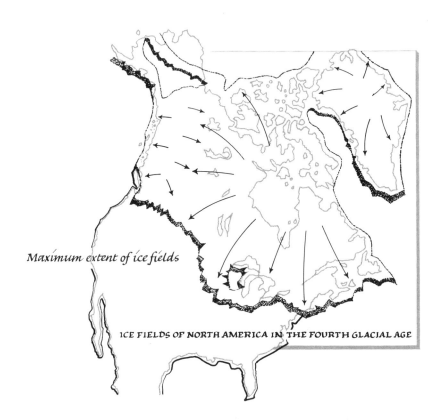

Maximum extent of ice fields

ICE FIELDS OF NORTH AMERICA IN THE FOURTH GLACIAL AGE

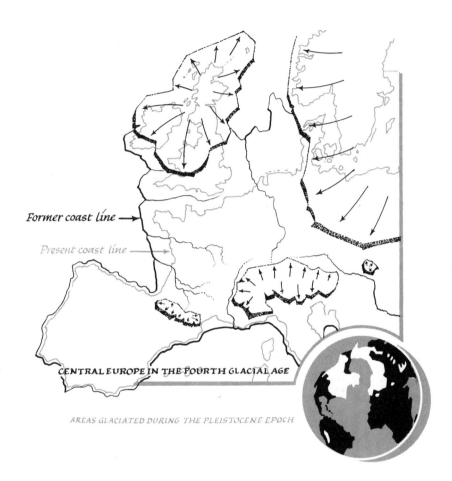

Former coast line →

Present coast line →

CENTRAL EUROPE IN THE FOURTH GLACIAL AGE

AREAS GLACIATED DURING THE PLEISTOCENE EPOCH

Undated Pictures

IN THE NINETEENTH CENTURY a marvelous collection of animal paintings was discovered on the ceiling of the limestone Altamira cave in northern Spain. Marked in with charcoal, painted in soft yellows and browns with colored minerals, these pictures —which included such large animals as a doe, a horse, and great bison—had remained, sealed away, for perhaps a hundred centuries. The Ice Age glaciers had not reached that far. When those paintings were made, *perhaps* the entire north part of Europe was still under glacial ice and the animals were living south of the ice edge. What was the date? The display was magnificent, but the paintings could not be dated.

Cave paintings have also been discovered in southern France. Reindeer and horses are among the animals pictured this time, indicating, *perhaps*, that the glaciers were retreating and the weather was becoming milder. Again the display was magnificent, but the paintings could not be dated.

Still more recently, cave paintings have been discovered in northern Africa. Antelope and wild sheep appear in groups, and hunters are shown also. The time of the paintings is *perhaps* later than the close of the European Ice Age. The pictures are wonderful, but they cannot be dated.

Cave of Altamira, Santander, Spain

Cave of Lascaux, France

Cave of Font-de-Gaume, France

Dordogne, France

Using Carbon

In North America as the Ice Age closed and the glaciers began to retreat under the summer heat, soil deposits formed each summer at the glacier edge. These layered deposits, called *varves*, resemble in many ways the growth rings of trees and so could show the years of melting. But the varves stopped forming when the glacier was gone, so the historical record would not extend to the present century. *Under such varves have been found the tools of early man and the charcoal of his campfire.* The striations of the varves were many and they could be counted, but the record stopped too soon. The age of the stone tools and the date of the campfire could not be decided with accuracy.

Other findings have been discovered in ancient caves or caught under lava flows. But always the dating was indefinite. And, always, there seemed no way to set up a common dating schedule for the events of North America, Europe, north Africa, and southwestern Asia.

VARVE FORMATION

Varve section from the bottom of a glacial lake, showing characteristic striations formed during four years of melting and freezing

Dark winter layer of colloidal particles precipitated after lake and its feeding streams froze

Light summer layer of heavier, angular particles

Carbon-14

VERY RECENTLY a new approach has been perfected to date ancient events. It has to do with the chemical element *carbon* as found in trees, and with two forms of the carbon atom.

I shall handle the part about the carbon in trees by mentioning a piece of firewood that I have in my hand, ready to be put into the fireplace. The tree from which it was cut last winter was then forty-two years old. I am sure of the age. The tree produces one growth ring each year and there are forty-two such rings from the center to the bark surface. In this particular piece of wood the central heartwood ring was placed in position forty-two years ago when the tree was a mere sapling. The next ring went in a year later, and so on. This means that all of the tree was not forty-two years old when cut; only the very center was.

The tree, as a marvelous chemist, interweaves carbon atoms with hydrogen and oxygen atoms. Carbon atoms for the formation of wood come directly from the carbon dioxide of the air. So the inside heartwood ring was built from carbon atoms obtained from the carbon dioxide of the air forty-two years ago. For the next layer the carbon atoms had been secured forty-one years ago. Thus the carbon atoms in the wood rings are arranged in the order of their year-by-year addition from carbon dioxide of the air.

We now turn our attention to the air. The carbon dioxide particles in it are relatively few compared with

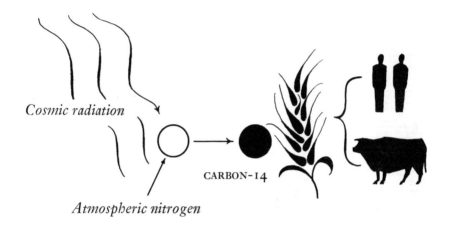

Cosmic radiation

CARBON-14

Atmospheric nitrogen

Carbon-14 combines with oxygen to form carbon dioxide and is absorbed by plants. Absorption stops at death.

AMOUNT OF CARBON-14 REMAINING

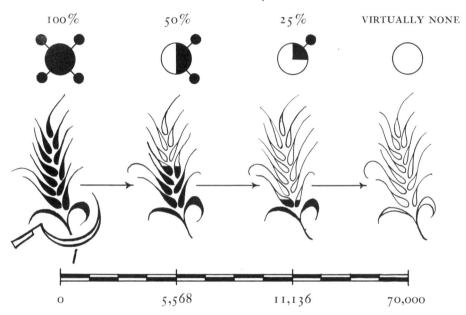

AGE IN YEARS AS DETERMINED BY RADIO-CARBON ACTIVITY

other air particles. The trees, however, are always able to get ample supplies for wood formation no matter at what point of the earth's surface the trees are growing.

Up high in the air an odd thing happens to carbon and nitrogen atoms. Some extra-heavy carbon atoms are being *created*. Cosmic rays from outer space strike nitrogen atoms and produce a nuclear transformation that changes the nitrogen atoms to carbon atoms. These are not ordinary carbon atoms of 12 weight units but extraordinary ones of 14 weight units, called *carbon-14*. This newly created carbon unites with oxygen in the air to produce carbon dioxide. This carbon dioxide, stirred by air currents, reaches the trees along with the far more numerous particles of common carbon dioxide. The tree treats both types of carbon dioxide in exactly the same chemical way. So into the heartwood of forty-two years ago the tree packed away the carbon-12 and the carbon-14 atoms in the same proportion that the two types of carbon dioxide existed in the air that reached the leaves of the tree.

The carbon-14 atoms have a peculiarity. They go back to nitrogen atoms again. For each atom the change when it occurs is like a miniature explosion. But for a mass of such atoms the change is a very drawn-out affair. *Half of the carbon-14 atoms of today will still be left 5,000 years from now!*

As the carbon-14 atom changes to a nitrogen atom the miniature explosion produces a click in a highly sensitive Geiger counter. Now for the use of such knowledge in dating a piece of ancient wood. No living tree is this old, but suppose there were a tree having a first growth ring formed 5,760 years ago and a last growth ring formed this year. Then a sensitive Geiger counter held to a small piece of the earliest ring would register just half as many clicks per second as it would for an equally heavy piece of the latest ring. This will be true because after 5,760 years only half of the original carbon-14 atoms remain in the wood.

Though no living tree has such a great age as 5,760 years, a piece of charcoal or the charred seeds of wheat from around some ancient campfire could have formed the woody parts of a plant that lived that long ago. For a piece of wood or charcoal of *unknown age* it would merely be necessary to count the clicks in a minute, compare the number with the results for the 5,760-year-old wood and the one-year-old wood, then—with the aid of a simple formula—calculate the age.

The Radiocarbon-Dating Process

Dr. Willard Libby, then at the University of Chicago, worked out a successful way to make use of carbon-14 atoms in finding the age of wood or charcoal fragments. He checked his results for accuracy against the tree-ring record of a giant sequoia cut down in 1874. This tree, known as the Centennial Stump, had started its growth—as determined by a count of its tree rings—in the year 1031 B.C. The fragment of wood tested by Dr. Libby spanned rings that had grown in the period from 1031 to 928 B.C. His experimental results gave an age to this fragment of 2,710 years. The actual age was about 200 years beyond that.

The relative closeness of the values promised an exciting future for the new procedure.

Since those early experiments, the process has been modified slightly to get even closer results. (A *possibility* exists that the cosmic rays from outer space may have varied by one or two percent at a few times in the long life of the giant sequoia. Had there been such a situation, the variation of a century between the experimental value and the actual one would be explainable.)

For his development of the new dating process, Dr. Libby received the Nobel Prize in chemistry in 1960. Today his laboratory is at the University of California. At it, and in several other laboratories in the United States and other countries, scientists are busy testing samples of wood or charcoal to get dates for events in history that were never dated before. Some accomplishments of such a laboratory devoted to historical research are narrated in a well-illustrated article in the *National Geographic* Magazine of August, 1958.[1] A conclusion given in the article should be noted: "Radiocarbon can date a tree and tell approximately when it died, but it can only *suggest* when the wood was turned into a beam, or a coffin, or a piece of charcoal. Interpretation by the archeologist must begin at that point."

[1] "How Old Is It?" by L. J. Briggs and K. F. Weaver, pages 234-255.

Draco

14

EXPLORING HISTORY

WITH

TREE-RING RECORDS

The giant sequoia already mentioned had been more than a century old when David was king of Israel and Judah. When cut it had lived for 2,905 years. During those 29 centuries this monarch of the California forests had kept, as growth rings, a year-by-year record of its life. Its development had not been completely steady through the centuries, for a succession of thick growth rings was often followed by perhaps a century of thin rings, after which the thick rings would appear again. The thick rings were evidently formed in peri-

[149]

ods of heavy rain, the thin ones in periods of reduced rainfall. But why did a heavy-rain period extend for as much as a century, to be followed by a century or so of reduced rainfall? In a historical way, what would such long-time variations in rainfall mean in human life?

A 3,000-Year Weather Chart for California

IN THE YEARS 1911 and 1912 the stumps of about 450 sequoia trees that had been cut for lumber were examined, their growth rings counted and measured. The Centennial Stump was one of these. A great majority of the trees had been between 1,000 and 2,000 years old when cut; 79 were between 2,000 and 3,000; three were over 3,000. These trees, like all sequoias in California, lived at a mile-high elevation along the western slope of the Sierra Nevadas. The soil is very deep. In this area rain falls only in winter. The trees grow in summer. But the amount of growth does not depend entirely upon the previous winter's rain, for the deep soil acts as a partial reservoir for the water from other years.

After the nearly 450 trees had been examined and their growth rings measured, a composite of the growth record for each year was determined and the results expressed as a curve. For convenience, the curve on page 152–3, has the growth records of the first thousand years separated from those of the second and third thousand years.

In that part of the curve that represents the two

thousand years from 100 B.C. on, there is a dip from about A.D. 70 to shortly before 1000, the bottom of the dip coming at about the year 630. In very slightly over three centuries, in the period from 1000 to 1310, the growth curve rises to form two sharp peaks with deep valleys between. After 1550 the peaks that appear are less lofty and much closer together. Throughout the record we can assume that the peaks were for cool years as well as rainy ones, and that the dips represented warm and dry ones.

Rainfall and History

THE SEQUOIAS SUPPLIED INFORMATION only about California. Did the same general conditions exist elsewhere? To check on the matter for Europe, here are the results, gleaned from history books, as they relate to three sharp-peak positions that appear on the sequoia weather chart: the century following 1200 B.C., the time close to A.D. 1000, and the one coming after A.D. 1310.

According to the history accounts, the century following 1200 B.C. was a period of great unrest in southeastern Europe. Semibarbarous tribes from the north broke through into the land that we know as Greece, seeking new pastures for their sheep. The same period of violent unrest, brought about, apparently, by a sharp change of climate, sent the Italian herdsmen over the mountain passes into Italy. With certain other tribes, shifts were made by boat to new home locations along the Mediterranean. In about two centuries the period of deep unrest had passed.

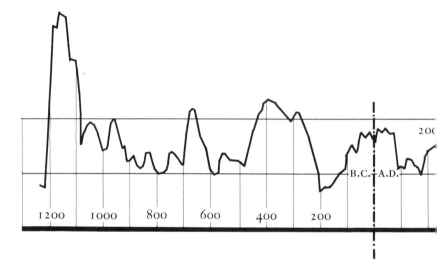

THE SEQUOIA RAINFALL RECORD

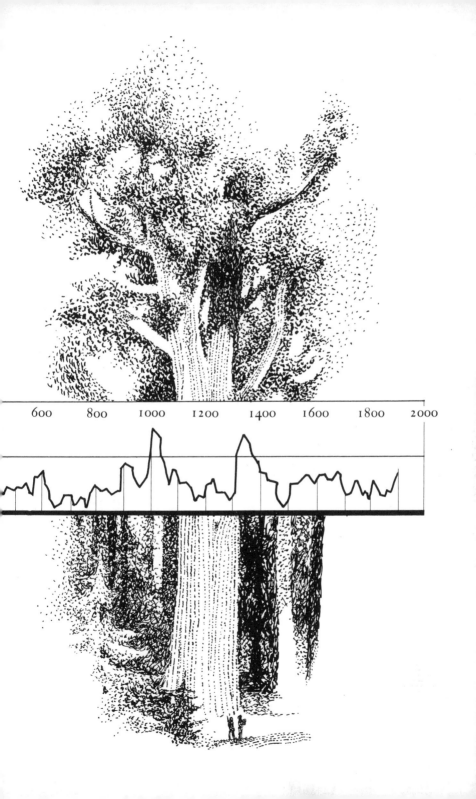

600   800   1000   1200   1400   1600   1800   2000

The second peak to be discussed, that of A.D. 1000, was the time of Viking unrest. Almost suddenly the climate of the north countries of Europe changed. Wet, cold rains drenched the land year after year, keeping the crops from ripening, drowning out the valley farms, keeping the cattle pastures soggy and useless. The desperate Vikings, Northmen, and Danes got into their fighting boats and sailed away. England was attacked. Northmen took over a part of France, calling it Normandy after themselves. In the Mediterranean a group of Vikings took the island of Sicily and ruled it. At that time, Leif Ericson sailed off to the west with his Vikings, then sailed back again. In less than half a century after the year 1000, the rains had decreased, warmer weather had returned, and the Viking raids had ceased.

The third weather peak to be discussed through history came a little over three centuries after the Viking unrest. It affected more people—who were sure that the world was coming to an end—and had effects that lasted longer. By 1308 incessant rains and stormy summers swept England and the European continent. By 1312 there was an almost complete failure of crops everywhere. In 1315-16 England had the greatest famine ever experienced—a famine brought on by too much water, not by too little. In 1322 the winter was so cold in Europe that the entire Baltic was frozen over, horse-drawn sleighs crossing regularly on the ice between Sweden and Germany. In other years the Rhine and the Thames were frozen over for weeks or months at a time, and fearful storms altered the coastlines of the North Sea and Baltic. Toward the close of this terrible century the Black Plague struck Europe, killing people by the tens of thousands. It was not until 1400 that the rainy, cold weather passed.

Weather in America

IN THE FOUR AND A HALF CENTURIES that have passed since the discovery of the New World, the rainfall pattern appearing on the sequoia weather chart has some distinctive features. Small sharp peaks rise like the teeth of a saw, from sixty to seventy-five years apart. Sharply-cut valleys lie between the peaks. With a general downward trend the tooth-shaped pattern moves to a period of very light rainfall about 1850. Referring to American history, we note that the people who crossed the plains in 1849 encountered terrible drouth conditions. Following this dry period, a rainfall peak comes about 1871. At this period Great Salt Lake became filled to the highest level in the memory of the white man.

The sequoia record made from the stumps of cut trees came to an end about 1901. Since then, Weather Bureau records for California have been used to extend the old record. The additional information shows the deep valley of the Great Drouth, which by 1931 had covered virtually all of the United States. Since then, a new but rather low peak has been forming. *Perhaps* there may be a new trough by 1995.

Revealing Tree Rings of the Southwestern Pines

AT SEVERAL LOCATIONS in New Mexico, Arizona, and adjoining states are to be seen the ruins of very old community dwellings nestled in shallow cavelike places along steep canyon walls, the rocks above the caves blackened from the rising smoke of the open fireplaces of centuries ago. Piled-up blocks of stone formed the rooms under the cave walls. Ceilings for the rooms were made from rows of poles, the spaces between the poles filled with straw. In these community structures higher tiers of rooms were built on those below, with the ceilings of the lower ones forming the floors of those above. To reach the upper levels, ladders made from slender tree trunks—with the stumps of cut-off limbs used as steps for the ladders—were leaned against the outside of the homes below. All cooking was done on smooth ground beyond the homes, near the cave walls. For the men of the community a round underground room was provided in front of the community location. The space for this room would first be excavated, then covered with heavy timbers for a ceiling. This was a ceremonial room, a sort of men's club, that the women were not allowed to enter. The cultivated fields for the community's crops of corn, beans, and squashes would not be too far away, and there would be pens for turkeys.

The largest and oldest of the canyon-wall communities of the Southwest has now been cleared of the sands that drifted in after it was abandoned. Now called by the Spanish name of Pueblo Bonito and set apart as the Chuco Canyon National Monument, this colossal community dwelling is in northern New Mexico. The site is not a part of any main stream channel and today very little water ever flows along the almost level stream bed between the canyon walls. No pines now grow along the hills; no crops could now be produced.

Standing today looking at the "Lost City" we may wonder about its history. At what rainy period of the past were the pines there, to be used for the ceiling poles and the timbers of the ceremonial room? At what period of drouth was the location deserted? Dr. A. E. Douglass of the University of Arizona developed the way by which the trees in the ruins were to answer those questions. By examining the timbers and poles still existing within the structure, counting the growth rings and noting whether wear had removed any of the outer growth rings, he was able to prove that Pueblo Bonito had been occupied for a little over two centuries. But the trees, in themselves, could not answer the question as to how long ago in years the occupancy had occurred.

The tree-ring records for other abandoned ruins of the same general type were also studied. These showed that the Mesa Verde cliff dwellings in southwestern Colorado were occupied for nearly two centuries, that these had been started somewhat later than Pueblo Bonito, and abandoned later. The same was true for White House Pueblo in eastern Arizona. But here, again, the trees, in themselves, could not indicate the

period of historical time when these locations were occupied.

It is now known that after these locations had been deserted rains came again to the Southwest. Some of the home sites established after the rains came have continued on in use down to the present time. By using the evidence of the trees as given by tree rings, a time schedule has been developed for this part of the history of the Southwest.

Then came the finally successful search for some tree or trees whose life or lives could bridge the years between the desertion of the cliff dwellings and the established recent history. Then a continuous history record could be built for the Southwest. How the search was carried out and how the discovery of a charred beam bound the two parts of the history together has been told by Dr. Douglass in an illustrated article in the December, 1929, issue of the *National Geographic* Magazine under the title "The Secrets of the Southwest Solved by Talkative Tree Rings."

Dates for Pueblo Bonito

THE CEREMONIAL ROOM of Pueblo Bonito was completed in the year 919. The communal building showed several periods of enlargement. The greatest increase in size came between 1033 and 1092, with the height of the building boom in 1067. By 1127 it was still occupied. There is no evidence that the occupancy lasted beyond 1130.

To see how those dates of history check against the long-time sequoia tree-growth record, a portion of the California weather curve is repeated for the four centuries between 800 and 1200.

Assuming that the record of growth for the Southwestern pines agrees with that of the sequoias *in a general way*, it is evident that the 211-year occupancy of Pueblo Bonito fits into the peak period of cool, wet weather that in Europe kept the crops from ripening in the Northland and sent the Vikings on their raids. When the dry and warm period came again Pueblo Bonito was deserted. The record for the Mesa Verde community locations showed that they were occupied until 1262. Before the days of the long and intense drouth of 1276-99, shown by the small growth rings of the Southwestern pines, they had been deserted.

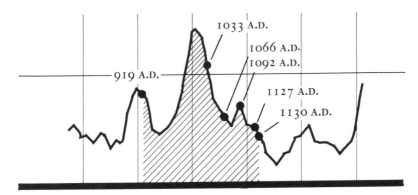

919 A.D.
1033 A.D.
1066 A.D.
1092 A.D.
1127 A.D.
1130 A.D.

PORTION OF RAINFALL CURVE RELATED TO OCCUPATION OF PUEBLO BONITO

The Land of the Mayas

LONG BEFORE EUROPEANS FIRST EXPLORED the Western Hemisphere, highly developed civilizations flourished. The Mayas, living in what is now Yucatán and Guatemala, are an outstanding example. They established a thriving agriculture, built an excellent network of roads, and raised temples that today remain marvels of architecture. But their most remarkable achievement was a calendar system unmatched—before or since—for precision.

The largest of the Mayan cities of Yucatán was Chichen Itzá. For more than four centuries, under the cultural leadership of Chichen Itzá, the Mayans made incredible advances in astronomy. Completely accurate predictions of the times of eclipses of the sun and the moon were worked out far in advance. Apparently they were also attempting to discover how to predict the coming of climatic changes from their records of a thousand years. We may surmise that certain changes of climate fitted in with the conjunctions of the planet Venus, for the priestly astronomers of those four centuries gathered an enormous amount of material on the motions of this planet. These efforts came to a sudden end when the Spaniards under Cortez conquered Mexico and Yucatán four and a half centuries ago. The time-recording plan used for over a thousand years by the Mayas and invented by them had been adopted by

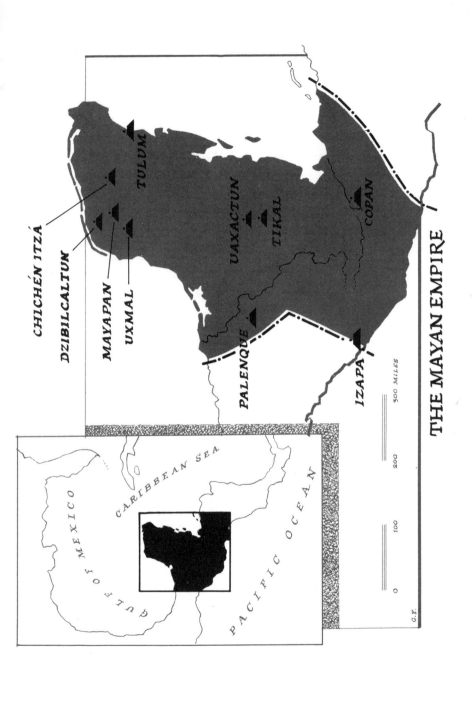

THE MAYAN EMPIRE

CHICHÉN ITZÁ

DZIBILCALTUN

MAYAPAN
UXMAL

TULUM

UAXACTUN

TIKAL

COPAN

PALENQUE

IZAPA

0   100   200   300 MILES

GULF OF MEXICO

CARIBBEAN SEA

PACIFIC OCEAN

G.F.

the Incas of far-off Peru and by the Aztecs of near-by Mexico several centuries before the coming of the Spaniards.

The Mayan Calendar and Time-Recording Plan

ON A MONOLITH found in the ruins of the old Mayan city of Tikal, Mayan hieroglyphics report an "inferior conjunction of Venus" for February 4, A.D. 452. How is the date known with such extreme preciseness? Because, like other Mayan astronomical facts appearing on monoliths, *the report was dated.*

The drawing shows the date that appears on the Tikal monolith, as expressed in numbers and names. The name *Muan* is that of a "month" of 20-day length, 18 of which made up 360 days of the year, to be followed in their plan by a short month of 5-day length, also named, that enlarged the year to 365 days. Muan was "month" number fifteen. The *Ahau* was a part of the "week" plan for the year. Each "week" had 13 days and there were enough weeks, all named, to cover a year of 364 days. Ahau was the name of the twentieth "week."

There was one point about this double measuring plan of marking off days in "months" and "weeks" that we would have encountered in an exactly similar way if our weeks were numbered. The "month" plan covered a year of 365 days while the "week" plan stopped at a year of 364 days. Both plans ran on continuously, so the shorter year kept drawing away from the beginning of the other year, a day at a time. In 365 years

DATE FROM THE TIKAL STELE

6 AHAU

13 MUAN

END OF KATUN 14

*(In the numbering, each bar represents 5,
each ball represents 1.)*

the shorter year would have advanced a whole year; so at intervals 365 years apart the two year arrangements would have their beginnings at the same time.

Twenty 365-day years gave the time interval of a *Katun*. The lowest part of the Mayan date design was, then, for the time in years from some starting time in history. We use the year of Christ's birth as such a starting time, the Mohammedans use the Hegira of Mohammed as such a time. The Mayas used 3300 B.C., but why they took a date as far back as that of Menes, the Egyptian, is difficult to understand.

Imix · Ik · Akbal · Kan · Chicchan · Cimi · Manik · Lamat · Muluc · Oc

Chuen · Eb · Ben · Ix · Men · Cib · Caban · Eznab · Cauac · Ahau

Pop · Uo · Zip · Zotz · Tzec · Xul · Yaxkin · Mol · Chen

Yax · Zac · Ceh · Mac · Kankin · Muan · Pax · Kayab · Cumhu · Uayeb

V

Nature's Seasons and the Calendar; A Concluding Section

Pegasus

15

SPRING AND SPRINGTIME

THE ADVANCE OF *spring* from the time of the spring equinox to that of the summer solstice, as viewed on the calendar or shown by the rising position of the sun toward its highest position in the sky, is completely steady and completely resistant to changes.

But the advance of *springtime*—that time of the year when living things, stimulated by the increasing warmth, burst into increased activity—is neither completely steady nor free from year-to-year variations. Thus the sun's position on such a spring day as April 1 can be predicted with full accuracy long before the event. But the top temperature that will be reached that day, the nest-building progress of the birds, the leaf sizes of the oaks, and all of the other responses of life to springtime can never be subject to an accurate prediction.

The Temperature Chart of Springtime

THE SUN IS NOT DIRECTLY RESPONSIBLE for the variations in temperature that occur on the same calendar date of different years.

The United States Weather Bureau has charted the temperature records for numerous parts of the country. One such chart shows the maximum temperature reached on each calendar day, *as averaged for thirty years of temperature recording.* Connected into a curve the day-by-day record is called the *normal* top-temperature curve. Such a curve, prepared from Weather Bureau records, is shown for the months of February through May for the city of Seattle. Notice the smoothness of this normal temperature curve. In a second curve the *actual* day-by-day high temperatures for the same months of the year 1960 are shown with the normal curve. How unsteady the actual temperatures have been! Undulations appear in the curve that can remind one vaguely of waves, each wave starting with extra-warm days, followed by extra-cold days, then finishing with extra-warm days again. Three undulations appear, the first approximately twice as long as each of the other two.

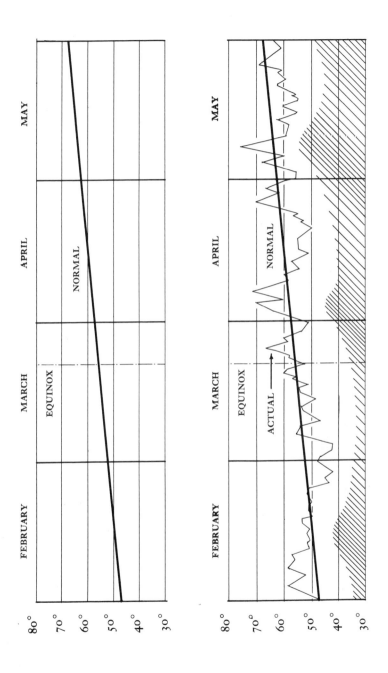

Long undulations reflect world-wide conditions of weather. (Thus the great American drouth period of the early 1930's, with its high temperatures and extremely low precipitation, was represented in Australia by the wettest and coolest years of the century.) Undulations of two-month length will affect portions of the United States, giving one portion of the country dry and hot weather while some adjoining portion is moist and cool. Pulsations of a week-length size are associated with the movement across the whole country or parts of it of cold fronts, whose progress will be shown on the Weather Bureau's daily weather charts.

A PERSONAL POSTLUDE

As I GATHER UP THE PAGES that I have written, the calendar on the wall reminds me in its printed way that it is

ONE   WEEK   TO   MAY

I know that when this May comes the sun overhead will be where it was on the first day of May a year ago, or a hundred years ago. It will rise in the east and set in the west at exactly the same minute that it did on the first of May many decades ago. Just an old sun, it would seem, in an old sky, repeating the May days that have come before.

But I know also that this May when it comes will be, for the world, a new May, a fresh May, a May that was never duplicated with exactness in any May before. The May of the calendar is predictable, that of nature's actual world is only partially predictable. We can have both Mays in mind when we say, "May is a wonderful month to enjoy!"

INDEX

INDEX

INDEX

Nut, and year of Thoth, 21-24

October, in Roman calendars, 86, 87, 88
Ovid, 79

Passover, feast of, 60-61, 101-102
paternity case, ancient, 21-24
Peru, Incas of, 164
Petrie, Flinders, 35
Philip, Alexander, 79-80
pines, Southwestern, 156-160
Pleistocene epoch, 132-133
Plutarch, 21-22, 79
Polaris, 121
pole star, 118, 120-122, 123
Pueblo Bonito, 157-160
    rainfall curve, 161
pulse rates, 20-21
pyramids, see Great Pyramid

Ra, year of, 21-24
radiocarbon dating process, 146-147
rainfall, tree-ring records of, 149-161
religious calendar, 61
Romance of Weights and Measures (Irwin), 35n, 109n
Roman Empire, 78-79, 124-125
    calendars of, 79-89, 91-93, 95, 97, 111
    and names of days, 108

Sabbath, the, 59, 60-61, 92
Saturday, the name, 107
seasons:
    and Babylon astronomy, 70-71
    length of, 8-10, 111
    in Moses' calendar, 60
    of nature, 171-176
    time cycles of, 2, 6-10
Seattle, Wash., temperature chart of, 172-173
seconds, arrangements of, 41, 43, 69-70

September:
    autumn equinox in, 6, 10
    in Roman calendars, 86, 87, 88
sequoia trees, 146-147
    weather chart from, 150-153, 155, 160
seven-day week, calendar of, 43, 57-61, 74, 92-93, 106-108
    and Comte's proposal, 110-111
Sirius, measurement by, 36, 68-69
Skalds Kaparmal, 109
solar calendar:
    of Moses, 74
    of Thoth, 37-38
solar year, 16, 37-38, 52, 54
    and seven-day week, 57-61
solstice, 8-10
    summer, 8
    winter, 8, 86, 102-104
Sosigenes, 84, 95
Southwest, tree-ring records in, 156-160
Spain, cave painting in, 134, 135
spring, of calendar, 10
    vs. springtime, 171-176
spring equinox, 6, 10
    and Easter, 96, 101-102
    and Moses' calendar, 60-61
    and Roman calendar, 86
    in Thoth calendar, 38-39
spring tides, 15
stars, study of, see astronomy
summer:
    length of, 10, 71
    in time cycle, 6
summer solstice, 8
sun:
    in Babylon astronomy, 71
    and earth's orbit, 8-9, 16
    and moon's orbit, 10, 12-13
    and time cycles, 5-10, 25
    see also solar
Sunday, the name, 108

telescope, of Khufu, 34, 36, 118-119, 121-122

A NOTE ON MANUFACTURE

THE TEXT OF THIS BOOK was set on the Linotype in a face called JANSON, a robust "Old Face" of the Dutch school. Having in mind the wandering proclivities of the early punch-cutters, we can note with interest that this type was cut in Amsterdam by a Hungarian named Nicholas Kis, *circa* 1690. It was erroneously named for the Dutchman Anton Janson, who had been employed in Leipzig where the original matrices were discovered years later. These same mats are today in the possession of the Stempel Foundry, Frankfurt, and the version you are reading was modeled directly on type produced from the original strikes.

This book was composed by Ruttle, Shaw & Wetherill, and printed by Halliday Lithograph Corporation. S. D. Warren Company, manufactured the paper. The typography and binding designs are by Guy Fleming.

The 365 Days

THE SEQUOIA RECORD

PUEBLO BONITO

Yucatán : The Mayan Calendar

PAINTED CAVES